Junior Maths

Book 2

GALORE PARK

Junior Maths
Book 2

David Hillard

Series Editor: Louise Martine

www.galorepark.co.uk

Published by Galore Park Publishing Ltd
19/21 Sayers Lane, Tenterden, Kent TN30 6BW

www.galorepark.co.uk
Text copyright © David Hillard 2008
Illustrations copyright Galore Park 2008

Layout by Typetechnique
Technical illustrations by Simon Tegg
Cartoon illustrations by Gwyneth Williamson
Cover design by The Design Gallery

Printed by Replika Press Pvt Ltd, India

ISBN: 978 1 905735 23 5

First published 2008, reprinted 2008, 2009, 2010, 2011, 2012

To accompany this course:
Junior Maths Book 2 Answer Book   ISBN: 978 1 905735 24 2
Junior Maths Book 2 Teacher's Resource   D0122008
Available for download from www.galorepark.co.uk

Details of other Galore Park publications are available at www.galorepark.co.uk

ISEB Revision Guides, publications and examination papers may also be obtained
from Galore Park.

The publishers are grateful for permission to use the photographs as follows:

Chapter 1: page 12 Peter Horree/Alamy; Chapter 12: page 121 Derek Croucher/
Alamy; Chapter 16: page 175 UK21/Alamy; Chapter 17: page 184 Oxford Picture
Library/Alamy; Chapter 21: page 244 Skyscan Photolibrary/Alamy; Chapter 23:
page 264 Alvey & Towers Picture Library/Alamy

About the author

David Hillard has spent more than 45 years teaching Mathematics in two preparatory schools. Generally he has taught those who would not describe themselves as particularly proficient at the subject.

Since 1980 he has been associated with the Common Entrance Examination at 11+, 12+ and 13+ levels in the role of either adviser, assessor or setter. He played a significant part in the revision of the syllabus in 2003 when the present format of the examination was introduced.

He is a co-author of the successful *Fundamental Mathematics* series, first published in 1984.

Preface

This book is aimed at Year 4 pupils. The emphasis is on providing a thorough and sound basis of the number work and other topics required at this stage. While emphasising a firm foundation there is plenty of extension work to engage and stretch the more able. There is material for all abilities.

The book continues the philosophy of the first in this series – a combination of the contemporary 'mental' approach and the more 'traditional' methods. In the final analysis it is the interests of the pupil that are paramount. One technique will not be suitable for all pupils, so varied approaches are explored.

Once again, there is no prescribed teaching order and it is anticipated that a chapter will be revisited during the course of the year. Teachers know best what to do and when to do it in order to help their pupils succeed.

The useful chapter on Mental Strategies from Book 1 has been repeated here, but without the exercises. Each chapter ends with an activity in the form of a freestanding diversion, and a piece of trivia knowledge intended to enlighten the learning process.

Acknowledgements

When I started this project I was greatly motivated by my ex-colleagues at Wellesley House whom I mentioned in Book 1. Since its publication I have been hugely encouraged by its reception and the very kind words that have met its appearance. The writing is only a part of the undertaking. I owe so very much more to Galore Park and especially to Louise Martine who is, in modern parlance, my 'line manager'. The imagination and resources that she has used are very much appreciated. This also applies to all those who are nameless but whose expertise has been integral in the final analysis.

David Hillard
June 2008

Contents

Chapter 1: Place value

Look at the number 467

It has three digits (figures). We know that the value of each digit depends on its position or place in the number. Putting the number in columns helps us to understand the value of each digit. Each column has a different name (value).

Hundreds	Tens	Units
H	T	U
4	6	7

The position of each digit tells us its **place value**.

4 **Hundreds** 6 **Tens** 7 **Units** gives **four hundred and sixty-seven** in words.

We can also use the columns to help us write numbers in figures.

Example:

Write nine hundred and five in figures.

	Hundreds	Tens	Units
	H	T	U
9 hundreds	9		
0 tens		0	
5 units			5

gives **905** in figures.

Exercise 1.1: Writing numbers

1. Write these numbers in words:

   (a) 67

   (b) 80

   (c) 361

   (d) 450

   (e) 702

   (f) 866

2. Write down the real value of the underlined digit:

   (a) 3̲65　　　　　　　　(d) 21̲6

   (b) 40̲7　　　　　　　　(e) 18̲8

   (c) 3̲8　　　　　　　　　(f) 267̲

3. Write these numbers in figures:

   (a) Four hundred　　　　　　(d) Six hundred and fifty

   (b) Seventy-three　　　　　　(e) Two hundred and sixty-four

   (c) One hundred and forty-nine　(f) Three hundred and forty

Place value and larger numbers

We are now going to look at larger numbers. When there are more than three digits we move into **Thousands**. The thousands block has its own hundreds, tens and units.

Hundred thousands						Ten thousands					Thousands			
1	0	0	0	0	0	1	0	0	0	0	1	0	0	0

Again, each column is **10** times larger than its right-hand neighbour.

Note: A four-digit number is written with no spaces between the digits: 1234

When there are five or six digits in a number, a half space is left between the hundreds and thousands:

　　56 789
　123 456

. . . .

Exercise 1.2: Place value and larger numbers

Write down the real value of the underlined digit:

1. 4̲317　　　　　　4. 32̲ 643　　　　　　7. 1̲46 742

2. 2̲16 417　　　　　5. 14 7̲00　　　　　　8. 811̲9

3. 1̲4 500　　　　　　6. 143̲8　　　　　　　9. 7̲1 000

10. 123 4<u>56</u>   12. 1<u>23</u> 456   14. 1<u>23</u> 456

11. 123 45<u>6</u>   13. 123 4<u>5</u>6   15. <u>123</u> 456

We can write a number with thousands in words by putting the numbers into columns, as we did for smaller numbers.

● First, divide the figures into blocks of three, starting from the right.

● Then write each block in **Hundreds**, **Tens** and **Units**, putting 'thousand' where the break is.

Examples:

	Hundreds	Tens	Units	(thousand)	Hundreds	Tens	Units
(i)			2		1	7	4
			Two	thousand	one hundred and seventy-four		
(ii)		3	8		5	0	6
		Thirty-eight		thousand	five hundred and six		
(iii)	9	2	0		0	4	0
	Nine hundred and twenty			thousand	and forty		

Exercise 1.3: Writing larger numbers in words

Write these numbers in words:

1. 4125

2. 1732

3. 5981

4. 7138

5. 3640

6. 6027

7. 1500

8. 2598

9. 5050

10. 8005

11. 19 246	16. 32 108
12. 10 700	17. 51 275
13. 57 214	18. 12 600
14. 84 386	19. 75 000
15. 62 372	20. 43 010
21. 172 934	26. 842 497
22. 124 712	27. 162 534
23. 728 536	28. 243 020
24. 294 371	29. 200 160
25. 920 321	30. 101 010

We break the number at the 'thousand' in the same way when we write a number with thousands in figures.

● First break the number at the word **thousand**.

● Then write the number either side of the break as **Hundreds**, **Tens** and **Units**.

Tip: Be careful you remember to fill in the last three columns.

Examples:

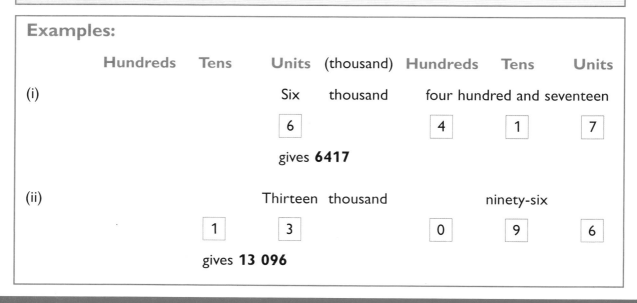

	Hundreds	Tens	Units	(thousand)	Hundreds	Tens	Units
(i)			Six	thousand	four hundred and seventeen		
			6		4	1	7
			gives **6417**				
(ii)		Thirteen	thousand		ninety-six		
	1	3			0	9	6
	gives **13 096**						

	Hundreds	Tens	Units	(thousand)	Hundreds	Tens	Units
(iii)		Four hundred and twenty-eight		thousand			
	4	2	8		0	0	0

gives **428 000**

Exercise 1.4: Writing larger numbers in figures

Write these numbers in figures:

1. Three thousand, six hundred and forty-nine
2. Eight thousand, three hundred and twenty
3. One thousand, two hundred and two
4. Five thousand, eight hundred and fifty-seven
5. Seven thousand
6. Three thousand, one hundred and five
7. Nine thousand, eight hundred and ninety
8. Three thousand, five hundred and one
9. Eight thousand six hundred
10. Three thousand and three
11. Eighteen thousand, three hundred and forty-eight
12. Twenty-seven thousand, one hundred and eighty-four
13. Fifty-nine thousand, six hundred and forty-two
14. Seventy-three thousand, nine hundred and one
15. Ninety-nine thousand, nine hundred and nineteen
16. Forty thousand

17. Thirty thousand four hundred

18. Fifty-three thousand and sixty

19. Eighty-one thousand and five

20. Nineteen thousand, two hundred and one

21. Two hundred and twenty-six thousand, five hundred and twenty-seven

22. Six hundred and twenty-five thousand, two hundred and thirteen

23. One hundred and twelve thousand, eight hundred and sixty-eight

24. Seven hundred thousand

25. Four hundred and twenty thousand, six hundred

26. Eight hundred and seven thousand and ninety

27. Three hundred and twenty-four thousand, two hundred and six

28. Two hundred and eight thousand, three hundred

29. Five hundred thousand and fifty

30. Six hundred and sixty thousand and six

Ordering numbers

The more digits a whole number has the larger it is.

> **Example:**   10 423 (5 digits) is larger than 9968 (4 digits)

If there is the same number of digits, **place value** decides the size of the number.

> **Examples:**
>
> (i)   3874 and 1862
>
>   Look at the **Thousands** digits   **3**874 and **1**862
>
>   3874 is larger because 3 thousands (3000) is larger than 1 thousand (1000).

(ii) 84 900 and 86 150

Both numbers start with 8, so look at the next digit (the **Thousands** digit)   84 900 and 86 150

86 150 is larger because 6 thousands (6000) is larger than 4 thousands (4000)

(iii) 172 491 and 172 438

Both numbers start with 1724, so look at the fifth digit (the **Tens** digit) 172 491 and 172 438

172 491 is larger because 9 tens (90) is larger than 3 tens (30)

Exercise 1.5: Ordering numbers

1. Write these numbers in order of size, starting with the **largest**:

(a) 17   3841   974

(b) 1483   627   2316

(c) 5142   7300   4901

(d) 7432   8569   8635

(e) 5839   5273   5493

(f) 6732   6730   6733

(g) 1567   5761   6715   7165

(h) 3486   8634   3468   8643

(i) 18 492   9479   20 873

(j) 41 685   40 175   59 723

(k) 39 568   37 392   38 700

(l) 73 291   73 037   73 146

(m) 84 264   84 269   84 263

(n) 12 345   34 512   12 543   34 125

(o) 26 481   26 841   26 184   26 148

(p) 86 092   86 045   86 054   86 029

(q) 120 987   129 308   12 642

(r) 743 289   863 517   356 284

(s) 165 859   165 895   165 589

(t) 683 192   652 072   672 135

(u) 342 168   341 168   332 168   323 168

(v) 123 456   231 546   312 654   132 465

(w) 109 386   109 380   109 385   109 384

(x) 4637   27 486   42 185   4819   143 209

(y) 87 142   87 348   87 329   87 064   87 175

(z) 643 216   643 612   643 162   643 621   643 126

2. Write these numbers in order of size, starting with the **smallest**:

(a) 37   1029   486

(b) 1528   389   954

(c) 3217   4210   2816

(d) 7916   7842   7019

(e) 4837   4828   4896

(f) 2945   2948   2819

(g) 1486   1480   1489   1490

(h) 3692   9236   2963   3629

(i) 26 217   9898   31 400

(j) 38 172   43 219   43 506

(k) 48 219   48 208   48 223

(l) 34 816   34 618   34 168

(m) 89 564   89 563   89 567

(n) 59 234   23 186   23 816   59 324

(o) 14 723   14 732   14 734   14 733

(p) 23 793   27 821   24 285   26 603

(q) 10 386   103 860   1038

(r) 421 963   583 206   349 862

(s) 518 729   586 175   562 987

(t) 374 291   374 921   374 192

(u) 172 486   173 841   178 341   174 831

(v) 310 567   310 675   310 576   310 765

(w) 123 456   234 561   561 234   435 162

(x) 106 300   83 251   2943   83 260   113 250

(y) 72 417   72 471   72 477   72 411   72 400

(z) 52 140   52 410   521 004   52 014   52 104

Exercise 1.6: Summary exercise

1. Using only the digits 4, 2, 8 and 6, write down:

    (a) the largest number you can;

    (b) the smallest number you can;

    (c) as many different 4 digit numbers as you can. (There are 24 of them. Try to think of a plan to use)

2. Write:

    (a) the number 24 310 in words;

    (b) three hundred and two thousand and sixteen in figures.

3. Write down the real value of the underlined digit:

  (a) 43 2̲16   (b) 2̲74 190   (c) 7̲0 000   (d) 108̲ 950

4. Write these numbers in order of size, starting with the **largest**:

  (a) 421 500   42 199   421 000

  (b) 43 100   34 160   43 000

  (c) 109 345   109 347   109 342   109 340

5. Write these numbers in order of size, starting with the **smallest**:

  (a) 327   1891   783

  (b) 9176   4832   4823   9167

  (c) 127 387   127 378   127 783   127 873

End of chapter activity: Binary arithmetic

Introduction to Binary arithmetic

You may be wondering what Binary arithmetic is. Well, it's connected with the development of computers and calculators.

During the Second World War (1939 – 45) it was vital to have as much warning as possible of both sea and air attacks. A team, led by Sir Robert Watson-Watt, developed *radar* (radio detection and ranging) as a way of finding possible threats.

The radar machines contained many valves which could be either *on* or *off*. When a valve was *on* it could be used to show the number 1. When a valve was *off* it could be used to show the number 0. A row of valves could therefore show a signal (number) such as 101101. Binary numbers such as this can be converted into decimal numbers, as shown below.

The use of binary numbers in radar helped with the development of computers, which work in a similar way. A computer can calculate large amounts of information using only combinations of the digits 1 and 0: from solving huge, complex equations to helping you with your maths homework!

In our denary, or decimal, system of counting we use 10 digits, 0 to 9

Binary, or base 2, arithmetic uses only 2 digits, 0 and 1

We are used to the column headings increasing 10 times (100, 10, 1).
In binary they increase 2 times. (In the example below the column headings
are **8**, **4**, **2** and **1**)

64	32	16	8	4	2	1

Since numbers are made up of only 0s and 1s, either the column is worth its
value or it is not, so it is easy to write binary numbers as decimal numbers.

Examples:

	8	4	2	1
(i)		1	0	1	= 4 + 0 + 1 = 5
		1 four	0 twos	1 one
(ii)	1	0	0	0	= 8 + 0 + 0 + 0 = 8
(iii)	1	1	1	1	= 8 + 4 + 2 + 1 = 15

Write these binary numbers as decimal numbers. Remember to use
the columns:

64	32	16	8	4	2	1

1. 10
2. 11
3. 100
4. 111
5. 1010

6. 1101
7. 1110
8. 10000
9. 10101
10. 11011

Now add an extra column or two on the left and make up some binary
numbers of your own. Swap your numbers with a partner and see if you get
the same decimal answers.

Did you know?

The railway station with the longest name in the UK is on the Welsh island of Anglesey:

Llanfairpwllgwyngyllgogerychwyrndrobwllllantysiliogogogoch

It has **58** letters but is more commonly known as Llanfairpwll or Llanfair PG.

Chapter 2: Counting

In this chapter we are going to look at counting in tens, hundreds and thousands, and see how this relates to the columns we saw in Chapter 1:

Hundreds	Tens	Units
H	T	U

Counting in tens

When we **count on** in **10s** we add 1 to the **Tens** column.

> **Examples:**
>
> (i)
>
> (ii)
>
> (iii) 230   240   250   260
>
> (iv) 480   490   500   510
>
> (v) 1210   1220   1230   1240
>
> Note: When we add 1 to 9 to get 10 (part (ii)) there is now a zero in the tens column.

When we **count back** in **10s** we subtract 1 from the **Tens** column.

> **Examples:**
>
> (i)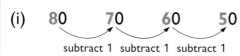
>
> (ii) 91   81   71   61
>   subtract 1 subtract 1 subtract 1
>
> (iii) 220   210   200   190
>
> (iv) 732   722   712   702
>
> (v) 1510   1500   1490   1480
>
> Note: When you reach 0 in the tens column (part (iii)) remember that you have to reduce the number of hundreds in the hundreds column by 1. In this case we have 1 hundred and 9 tens.

Exercise 2.1: Counting in tens

1. Count on six times in 10s starting from:
    (a) 72   (c) 285   (e) 3600
    (b) 160   (d) 1640   (f) 2215

2. Write down the answer to each of these calculations.
    (a) 24 + 70   (c) 167 + 60   (e) 1791 + 90
    (b) 83 + 50   (d) 284 + 40   (f) 980 + 30

3. Count back six times in 10s starting from:
    (a) 92   (d) 1030   (g) 6700
    (b) 130   (e) 2570   (h) 5105
    (c) 217   (f) 3425

4. Write down the answer to each of these calculations.
    (a) 51 – 30   (c) 326 – 40   (e) 5327 – 70
    (b) 103 – 50   (d) 3759 – 80   (f) 4600 – 20

Counting in hundreds

When we **count on** in **100s** we add 1 to the **Hundreds** column.

Examples:				Note: when we reach 9, adding a 1 to the hundreds column gives us 10. So 1 thousand and 0 hundreds.
(i) 500	600	700	800	
(ii) 840	940	1040	1140	
(iii) 7950	8050	8150	8250	

When we **count back** in **100s** we subtract 1 from the **Hundreds** column.

Examples:				Note: when we have a 0 in the hundreds column (part (ii)), we reduce the number in the thousands column by 1. In this case this gives us 4 thousands and 9 hundreds.
(i) 620	520	420	320	
(ii) 5000	4900	4800	4700	
(iii) 2200	2100	2000	1900	

Exercise 2.2: Counting in hundreds

1. Count on six times in 100s starting from:

   (a) 850

   (b) 1700

   (c) 2870

   (d) 3694

   (e) 9860

   (f) 8292

2. Write down the answer to each of these:

   (a) 259 + 600

   (b) 643 + 800

   (c) 1600 + 700

   (d) 2541 + 500

   (e) 7895 + 200

   (f) 5082 + 200

3. Count back six times in 100s starting from:

   (a) 1200

   (b) 3700

   (c) 4100

   (d) 2550

   (e) 10 300

   (f) 1090

4. Write down the answer to each of these:

   (a) 778 − 300

   (b) 1300 − 900

   (c) 2500 − 700

   (d) 3450 − 500

   (e) 12 100 − 600

   (f) 10 900 − 800

Counting in thousands

When we **count on** in **1000s** we add 1 to the **Thousands** column.

Examples:				Note: when we reach 9 (in part (i)), adding a 1 to the thousands column gives us 10. So 1 ten thousand and 0 thousands.
(i) 1000	2000	3000	4000	
(ii) 8800	9800	10 800	11 800	

When we **count back** in **1000s** we subtract 1 from the **Thousands** column.

Examples:				Note: when we have a 0 in the thousands column (part (i)), we reduce the number in the ten thousands column by 1. In this case this gives us 0 ten thousands and 9 thousands.
(i)	12 000	11 000	10 000	9000
(ii)	63 500	62 500	61 000	60 100

Exercise 2.3: Counting in thousands

1. Count on six times in 1000s starting from:

   (a) 7000

   (b) 14 700

   (c) 96 200

   (d) 346 000

   (e) 500 000

   (f) 800 000

2. Write down the answer to each of these:

   (a) 3456 + 6000

   (b) 5870 + 8000

   (c) 9700 + 6000

   (d) 51 580 + 8000

   (e) 38 230 + 5000

   (f) 42 500 + 4000

3. Count back six times in 1000s starting from:

   (a) 9000

   (b) 27 000

   (c) 81 500

   (d) 100 000

   (e) 810 000

   (f) 30 000

4. Write down the answer to each of these:

   (a) 5650 − 3000

   (b) 12 350 − 8000

   (c) 21 900 − 7000

   (d) 43 000 − 6000

   (e) 90 000 − 9000

   (f) 1860 − 900

Exercise 2.4: Summary exercise

Calculate the following:

1. 320 + 60
2. 497 + 30
3. 563 + 40
4. 1248 + 80
5. 2915 + 90

6. 460 – 50
7. 220 – 60
8. 410 – 80
9. 4250 – 70
10. 5010 – 90

11. 410 + 300
12. 680 + 500
13. 850 + 600
14. 1750 + 200
15. 4700 + 400

16. 950 – 700
17. 1200 – 300
18. 2450 – 800
19. 43 500 – 600
20. 61 000 – 900

21. 3400 + 6000
22. 9070 + 2000
23. 13 000 + 9000
24. 27 500 + 5000
25. 148 000 + 7000

26. 9500 – 3000
27. 10 600 – 7000
28. 21 000 – 8000
29. 42 400 – 6000
30. 130 000 – 2000

End of chapter activity: More binary arithmetic

In Chapter 1 we converted binary numbers into decimal numbers. This time we will convert the other way round, that is decimal into binary.

Do you remember the binary column headings?

| 64 | 32 | 16 | 8 | 4 | 2 | 1 |

If you can fill the column you put 1, if you cannot you put 0

Examples:

(i) Write 27 in binary

- Which is the largest column you can fill? Look at the column headings on the previous page and find the largest number that is less than 27

    Answer: 16

- Write out the headings, starting with 16

16	8	4	2	1

- Put a 1 in the **16** column.

16	8	4	2	1
1				

- Now subtract 16 from 27 to see what is left, 11

    27 − 16 = 11

    Fill in the largest column you can, the **8** column

16	8	4	2	1
1	1			

- What is left now?

    11 − 8 = 3

    You cannot fill the **4** column, so put a **0**

16	8	4	2	1
1	1	0		

- You can fill the **2** column, so put a **1**

16	8	4	2	1
1	1	0	1	

- What is left now?

    3 − 2 = 1

    Put a 1 in the **1** column

16	8	4	2	1
1	1	0	1	1

So 27 = 11011 in binary.

(ii) Write 50 in binary.

- The largest column needed is 32

32	16	8	4	2	1
1					

- Fill the **32** column

- 50 − 32 = 18 so fill the **16** column

1	1				

- 18 − 16 = 2 so 0 in the **8** and **4** columns

1	1	0	0		

- Fill the **2** column

1	1	0	0	1	

- Nothing left so 0 in the **1** column

1	1	0	0	1	0

So 50 = 110010

Write these decimal numbers as binary numbers.

1. 5
2. 10
3. 15
4. 24
5. 35

6. 43
7. 63
8. 70
9. 85
10. 100

Now make up some questions of your own and test your neighbour.

. . . .

Did you know?

No doubt you have heard about counting sheep if you cannot get to sleep.

The best country to do this is New Zealand, where there are more sheep than people.

Chapter 3: Addition

By now you should be very familiar with the idea of adding. Sometimes you might do it in your head, but at other times you might write your calculations down on paper. If you need to remind yourself of some ways to add in your head, have a look at Chapter 26: Mental strategies.

These mental strategies can also be used to help you add large numbers together. Let's have a look at an example.

Example: 2800 + 4600

Think of 2800 as (2000 + 800) or (3000 − 200)

Think of 4600 as (4000 + 600) or (5000 − 400)

So 2800 + 4600 = (2000 + 800) + (4000 + 600)

= (2000 + 4000) + (800 + 600)

= 6000 + 1400

= 7400

or 2800 + 4600 = (2000 + 800) + (5000 − 400)

= (2000 + 5000) + (800 − 400)

= 7000 + 400

= 7400

or 2800 + 4600 = (3000 − 200) + (4000 + 600)

= (3000 + 4000) + (−200 + 600)

= 7000 + 400

= 7400

1, 2, 3,

If the numbers you are adding are near to each other you might find it helpful to use **doubles**.

Example:	$8150 + 7980 = (8000 + 150) + (8000 - 20)$
	$= (8000 \times 2) + (150 - 20)$
	$= 16\,000 + 130$
	$= 16\,130$

Remember you may find it useful to use jottings along a number line.

Example: 1500 + 900

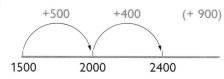

Giving an answer of $1500 + 900 = 2400$

Exercise 3.1: Addition

Calculate the following additions. Try to do as much as possible in your head. It may help to have pencil and paper ready to make some jottings.

1. 200 + 900
2. 800 + 600
3. 4000 + 2000
4. 9000 + 7000
5. 1700 + 6200

6. 4300 + 2500
7. 5600 + 2900
8. 2700 + 1500
9. 4700 + 3800
10. 7700 + 5200

11. 9300 + 6100
12. 4600 + 6800
13. 5700 + 9400
14. 3500 + 9500
15. 7900 + 4800

16. 3740 + 1230
17. 4130 + 2750
18. 1850 + 6150
19. 7250 + 1850
20. 2470 + 3160

21. 1680 + 7290
22. 4680 + 1780
23. 5790 + 2970
24. 8310 + 5430
25. 3780 + 8150

26. 7450 + 9560
27. 9750 + 8850
28. 5740 + 8310
29. 6480 + 3970
30. 8750 + 5500

31. 697 + 705
32. 459 + 465
33. 618 + 597
34. 925 + 887
35. 357 + 263

36. 1297 + 1301
37. 1495 + 1515
38. 3660 + 3570
39. 4525 + 4475
40. 10 017 + 9983

Formal addition

We can also do addition using a **formal method**. We put the digits into place value columns, and then add the numbers in each column.

Examples:

(i)　478 + 96

		H	T	U
		4	7	8
+			9	6
			1	4
		1	6	0
		4	0	0
		5	7	4

Step 1: Set out the digits in their correct columns.
Step 2: Add the **Units**. 8 + 6 = 14 units, or 1 ten and 4 units
Step 3: Add the **Tens**. 7 + 9 = 16 tens, or 1 hundred and 6 tens
Step 4: Add the **Hundreds** 4 + 0 = 4 hundreds
Step 5: Add your answers to steps 2, 3 and 4
to give the answer **574**

(ii) 783 + 529

	Th	H	T	U
			7	8	3
+		5	2	9
				1	2
			1	0	0
	1	2	0	0
	1	3	1	2

U   3 + 9 = 12 units, or 1 ten and 2 units

T   8 + 2 = 10 tens, or 1 hundred 0 tens

H   7 + 5 = 12 hundreds, or 1 thousand and 2 hundreds

Remember: You can check your answer to an addition by adding the numbers together in a different order. See how we can do this with example (ii).

Do you get the same answer?

	7	8	3
+	5	2	9

and

	5	2	9
+	7	8	3

There is another method of formal addition. It is very similar to the first method, but the calculation is shorter and quicker because we use **carrying figures.**

Example: 478 + 96

Step 1: Set out the digits in their correct columns.

	H	T	U
	4	7	8
+		9	6

Step 2: Add the **Units** 8 + 6 = 14

Write the 4 'units' in the answer row and carry the 1 'ten' to the **Tens** column

	H	T	U
			4
		1	

Step 3: Add the **Tens** plus the carried 1: 7 + 9 + 1 = 17

Write the 7 'tens' in the answer row and carry the 1 'hundred' to the **Hundreds** column

	4	7	8
+		9	6
		7	4
	1	1	

Step 4: Add the **Hundreds** plus the carried 1: 4 + 0 + 1 = 5

Write 5 'hundreds' in the answer row.

	4	7	8
+		9	6
	5	7	4
	1	1	

The **carrying figure** can be larger than 1

Example: 898 + 87 + 496

See how when we add the units: 8 + 7 + 6 = 21 we put the 1 'unit' in the **Units** column and carry the 2 'tens' to the **Tens** column

	Th	H	T	U
		8	9	8
			8	7
+		4	9	6
	1	4	8	1
		1	2	2

Exercise 3.2: Adding larger numbers

Calculate the following, using the formal method:

1.

	Th	H	T	U
		5	2	5
+			7	3

2.

	Th	H	T	U
		3	4	6
+		1	3	2

3.

	Th	H	T	U
		1	4	8
+			3	9

4. 427 + 165

5. 673 + 95

6. 384 + 172

7. 617 + 284

8. 827 + 106

9. 372 + 496

10. 538 + 197

11. 459 + 374

12. 432 + 912

13. 728 + 574

14. 376 + 624

15. 564 + 679

16. Add together 436 and 85

17. What is the sum of 156 and 248?

18. What number is 550 more than 690?

19. Increase 594 by 639

20. What is the total of 738 and 456?

21. 819 + 294

22. 449 + 876

23. 628 + 784

24. 236 + 987

25. 694 + 386

26. 326 + 148 + 219

27. 346 + 187 + 298

28. 827 + 768 + 529

29. 968 + 436 + 875

30. 492 + 27 + 132

31. 82 + 469 + 8

32. 277 + 5 + 96

33. 426 + 975 + 87

34. 247 + 6 + 94

35. 482 + 976 + 381

Problem solving

You can often use addition to solve a problem. You should use the method you feel most comfortable with.

Exercise 3.3: Problem solving

1. Mr Giles has a herd of 78 cows and a flock of 185 sheep.
   How many cows and sheep are there altogether?

2. It is 85 miles from London to Salisbury and 98 miles from Salisbury to Cardiff.
   How far is it from London to Cardiff via Salisbury?

3. The school library has 857 fiction books and 1785 non-fiction books.
   What is the total number of books in the library?

4. The Duke of Wellington was born in 1769 and died at the age of 83
   In what year did he die?

5. Chris scores 1286 runs in a season while his brother Graham scores 988 runs.
   What is their total number of runs during the season?

6. 238 people live in Lower Batty and 769 in Upper Batty.
   What is the population of the two villages?

7. Over the weekend the Piggy family eat 26 sticky buns, 19 doughnuts and 38 cream whirls.
   How many items does the family eat over the weekend?

8. James owns 65 toy cars, Kenny has 59 and Len has 6 more than the other two combined.
   How many toy cars does Len own?

9. The local Floral Society held an exhibition of its members' work. 285 came to view on Friday, 467 on Saturday and 386 on Sunday.
   How many came to view over the three days?

10. On Saturday, 39 864 people watched Manchester United. On Sunday, 38 363 watched Manchester City.
    How many watched the two games?

Exercise 3.4: Summary exercise

1. Calculate the following, using jottings where necessary:

   (a) 700 + 500

   (b) 350 + 430

   (c) 720 + 890

   (d) 4300 + 5200

   (e) 5700 + 1300

   (f) 3800 + 2600

   (g) 4280 + 3710

   (h) 384 + 376

   (i) 438 + 447

   (j) 1750 + 1870

2. Calculate the following, using the formal method:

   (a) 376 + 213

   (b) 426 + 137

   (c) 974 + 396

   (d) 496 + 187 + 63

   (e) 587 + 9 + 28

   (f) What is the sum of 486 and 917?

   (g) What number is 854 larger than 786?

   (h) Increase 784 by 859

   (i) Add together 365 and 487

   (j) What is the total when 738 and 487 are added together?

End of chapter activity: Magic squares

Magic squares were used by the Chinese thousands of years ago.

This is a magic square:

In a 3 x 3 magic square:

2	7	6
9	5	1
4	3	8

- the numbers 1 to 9 are used once each;

- each line (vertical, horizontal and diagonal) adds up to the same total.

What is the total in this example? Check each line does come to the same total.

How many different magic squares can you draw? (Keep the 5 in the centre.)

Look at your magic squares. Can you say anything interesting about magic squares?

Did you know?

A baker's dozen is 13, one more than a normal dozen (12).

In the thirteenth century, a baker who cheated his customers could have his hand chopped off by an axe.

To avoid this, bakers started giving 13 items for the price of 12 – just in case one was burnt or ruined in some way.

Chapter 4: Subtraction

Just as there are lots of different ways to add in your head, so you can subtract in your head using a variety of strategies. Have a look at Chapter 26: Mental strategies if you need to remind yourself of some of these methods.

In this chapter we are going to look at a number of different ways of working out your subtraction calculations on paper.

Complementary addition

The first method is called **complementary addition**. It might seem strange to talk about 'addition' when we want to subtract, but this method allows us to work out the answer to a **subtraction** calculation by **adding on** from the smaller number:

● Start with the smaller number.

● Add on numbers, step by step, until you reach the larger number.

● Add all these numbers together.

Example: 456 − 79

	H	T	U
	4	5	6
−		7	9
			1
		2	0
	3	0	0
		5	0
			6
	3	7	7

First set out your numbers in the correct columns.

Now start to add numbers to 79 with the aim of reaching 456

Try to make your calculations as easy as possible.

For example, you can start by adding 1, to make 80

Add 20 to make 100

Add 300 to make 400

Add 50 to make 450

Add 6 to make 456

Finally add together the numbers you have added to 79 to give the answer to the original subtraction
(1 + 20 + 300 + 50 + 6 = 377)

So, we have calculated that 456 − 79 = 377

You can reach the answer more quickly by adding larger totals. Let's look at 456 − 79 again.

Example: 456 − 79

	H	T	U
	4	5	6
−		7	9
		2	1
	3	5	6
	3	7	7

First set out your numbers in the correct columns.

Add 21 to make 100
Add 356 to make 456
Now add 21 + 356 = 377

Check that you can see why these examples work.

Examples:

(i) 846 − 375

	H	T	U
	8	4	6
−	3	7	5
		2	5
	4	4	6
	4	7	1

First set out your numbers in the correct columns.

Add 25 to make 400
Add 446 to make 846
Now add 25 + 446 = 471

(ii) 7146 − 2359

	Th	H	T	U
	7	1	4	6
−	2	3	5	9
			4	1
		6	0	0
	4	1	4	6
	4	7	8	7

First set out your numbers in the correct columns.

Add 41 to make 2400
Add 600 to make 3000
Add 4146 to make 7146
Now add 41 + 600 + 4146 = 4787

Remember: Check your answer by adding it to the number you subtracted. You should get the top number of your calculation. For example, if the last example above is correct, then 4787 + 2359 should equal 7146

Th	H	T	U
	4	7	8	7
+	2	3	5	9
	7	1	4	6
	1	1	1	

Yes it does!

Exercise 4.1: Subtraction by complementary addition

Calculate the following using the complementary addition method:

1.

Th	H	T	U
		6	0	0
–			6	7

2.

Th	H	T	U
		4	5	0
–			9	4

3.

Th	H	T	U
		3	2	0
–			8	7

4. 438 – 74

5. 829 – 47

6. 300 – 185

7. 700 – 247

8. 650 – 386

9. 740 – 123

10. 855 – 342

11. 486 – 274

12. 932 – 549

13. 671 – 483

14. 876 – 197

15. 710 – 248

16. 2000 – 67

17. 3000 – 23

18. 7500 – 87

19. 5000 – 540

20. 8000 – 420

21. 6500 − 870

22. 3750 − 375

23. 1380 − 643

24. 4830 − 916

25. 8460 − 758

26. 7000 − 3240

27. 6000 − 1672

28. 8300 − 1460

29. 2910 − 1325

30. 8562 − 4376

Compensation subtraction

Another way to subtract is to take away too much and then add on. This is called **compensation subtraction**. This time you start with the **larger number** and first take away an easy number. Then you make small changes to get the correct final answer. Let us look at some examples to see how it works.

Examples:

(i) 456 − 79

	H	T	U
	4	5	6
−	1	0	0
	3	5	6
+		2	1
	3	7	7

Write the larger number **only** in the correct columns

It is quite easy to subtract 100 from 456, to give 356

However, we only needed to subtract 79, so 100 is too much.

To compensate for this we need to add **21** back on, because 100 − 79 = 21

(ii) 846 − 375

	H	T	U
	8	4	6
−	4	0	0
	4	4	6
+		2	5
	4	7	1

Write the larger number **only** in the correct columns

Subtract 400

Add **25** back on, because 400 − 375 = 25

(iii) 7146 − 2359

	Th	H	T	U
	7	1	4	6
−	3	0	0	0
	4	1	4	6
+		6	4	1
	4	7	8	7

Write the larger number **only** in the correct columns

Subtract 3000

Add **641** back on, because 3000 − 2359 = 641

Exercise 4.2: Subtraction by compensation

Calculate the following using the compensation method:

1.

	H	T	U
	5	0	0
−		8	3

2.

	H	T	U
	3	5	0
−		7	6

3.

	H	T	U
	7	2	0
−		4	7

4. 325 − 68

5. 642 − 81

6. 700 − 146

7. 450 − 284

8. 830 − 417

9. 329 − 184

10. 920 − 453

11. 428 − 216

12. 849 − 574

13. 740 − 473

14. 561 − 287

15. 910 − 728

16. 1000 − 49

17. 4000 − 78

18. 3500 − 32

19. 7400 − 840

20. 2200 − 350

21. 5870 − 540

22. 7420 − 987

23. 8690 − 842

24. 6270 − 394

25. 1980 − 752

26. 8000 − 5480

27. 5000 − 3720

28. 4800 − 1960

29. 8650 − 3875

30. 4385 − 1848

Decomposition

Yet another method of subtraction is called **decomposition**. This involves breaking down (decomposing) the numbers.

Example: 456 − 79

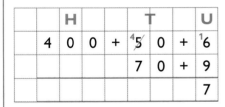

Step 1: First break down the numbers according to place value.

456 is the same as 400 + 50 + 6

79 is the same as 70 + 9

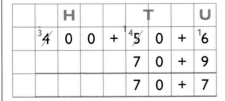

Step 2: Rewrite the calculation so that you can subtract the units easily. In this case you cannot subtract 9 from 6 so you have to **borrow** 10 from the **Tens** column to make 16

Now you can work out 16 − 9 = 7

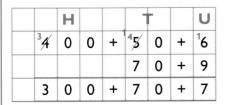

Step 3: You cannot subtract 7 from 4 so borrow 100 from the **Hundreds** column and work out 140 − 70 = 70

Step 4: 300 − 0 = 300

Step 5: Rewrite the answer in the normal way.

456 − 79 = 300 + 70 + 7 = 377

Formal subtraction

The **formal method** of subtraction is basically the same as decomposition. We still borrow from the next column along but we use a **carrying figure** instead of writing out the tens or hundreds in full.

Let's look at 456 − 79 again.

Example: 456 − 79

H	T	U
4	5	6
−	7	9

Step 1: Write the calculation in columns.

H	T	U
4	⁴5̸	¹6
−	7	9
		7

Step 2: Take 'ten' from the **Tens** column and add it to the **Units**. Now you can subtract the **Units**.
16 − 9 = 7

H	T	U
³4̸	¹⁴5̸	¹6
−	7	9
	7	7

Step 3: Now take 1 'hundred' from the **Hundreds** column and subtract the **Tens**. 14 − 7 = 7

H	T	U
³4̸	¹⁴5̸	¹6
−	7	9
3	7	7

Step 4: Now subtract the **Hundreds** 3 − 0 = 3

456 − 79 = 377

We follow exactly the same steps, however many columns the calculation has.

Example: 7468 − 2795

Th	H	T	U
	7	4	6	8
−	2	7	9	5

Step 1: Write the calculation in columns.

Th	H	T	U
	7	4	6	8
−	2	7	9	5
				3

Step 2: Subtract the **Units** 8 − 5 + 3

Th	H	T	U
	7	³4̸	¹6	8
−	2	7	9	5
			7	3

Step 3: Take 1 'hundred' from the **Hundreds** to calculate the 'tens' 16 − 9 = 7

Th	H	T	U
⁶7̸	¹³4̸	¹6	8
−	2	7	9	5
	6	7	3

Step 4: Take 1 'thousand' from the **Thousands** and calculate the 'hundreds' 13 − 7 = 6

Th	H	T	U
⁶7̸	¹³4̸	¹6	8
−	2	7	9	5
4	6	7	3

Step 5: Finally subtract the **Thousands**.

If there are zeros in the top line, we must be extra careful. It is important to work through each column in turn.

Example: 800 − 147

	H	T	U
	8	0	0
−	1	4	7

Step 1: Write the calculation in columns.

	H	T	U
	⁷8	¹0	0
−	1	4	7

Step 2: There are no **Tens** to take, so take 1 'hundred' from the **Hundreds** to add to the **Tens**.

	H	T	U
	⁷8	⁹0	¹0
−	1	4	7

Step 3: Now take 1 'ten' from the **Tens** (10 tens becomes 9 tens) and add it to the **Units**.

	H	T	U
	⁷8	⁹0	¹0
−	1	4	7
	6	5	3

Step 4: Now you can subtract the **Units**, then the **Tens**, and finally the **Hundreds**.

Exercise 4.3: Subtraction by decomposition or the formal method

Calculate the following using decomposition or the formal method.

1. 85 − 47
2. 90 − 34
3. 423 − 68
4. 162 − 89
5. 745 − 76

6. 826 − 159
7. 725 − 348
8. 431 − 294
9. 643 − 186
10. 926 − 749

11. 746 − 578
12. 527 − 189
13. 843 − 694
14. 655 − 287
15. 762 − 486

16. 218 − 159
17. 460 − 273
18. 100 − 38
19. 300 − 73
20. 400 − 127

21. 500 − 282
22. 406 − 87
23. 701 − 146
24. 3246 − 678
25. 2196 − 473

26. 3729 − 947
27. 7426 − 879
28. 4173 − 2686
29. 9786 − 6879
30. 4372 − 1864

31. 1000 − 483
32. 7000 − 2964
33. 5040 − 1786
34. 4058 − 3872
35. 7005 − 1627

Problem solving

Maths problems can often be solved using subtraction. Answer the questions in Exercise 4.4 using the methods you find easiest to use.

. . . .

Exercise 4.4: Problem solving

1. A tin contains 72 digestive biscuits. 24 of them are chocolate covered and the rest are plain.
    How many plain biscuits are there?

2. Fernando drives from London to Dover via Maidstone. It is 78 miles from London to Dover and 39 miles from London to Maidstone.
    How far is it from Maidstone to Dover?

3. Bobby plays darts. He needs to score a total of 501
    At present he has scored 356
    How many more does Bobby need to score to reach his goal?

4. In the vicar's Bible the Old Testament is 730 pages long and the New Testament contains 227 pages.
    How many pages longer is the Old Testament than the New Testament?

5. William Shakespeare was born in 1564 and died on his birthday in 1616
    How old was he when he died?

6. Admiral Nelson was aged 47 when he died at the Battle of Trafalgar in 1805.
    In what year was he born?

7. A theatre can seat 1225 people. On Tuesday there were 368 empty seats.
    How many seats were occupied on Tuesday?

8. In a shooting competition, Bernie scores 1164 points and Max scores 1079 points.
    How many more points does Bernie score?

9. It is 6010 miles from London to Cape Town. Jack takes off from London and lands at Nairobi. After a business meeting he flies the extra 2458 miles from Nairobi to Cape Town.
    What is the distance between London and Nairobi?

10. In the 4th round of the FA Cup, 26 003 people watched Sheffield United and 13 062 watched Sheffield Wednesday.
What was the difference in the size of the crowds?

. . . .

Exercise 4.5: Summary exercise

Calculate the following using an appropriate method.

1. 47 – 33
2. 81 – 37
3. 174 – 169
4. 304 – 197
5. 433 – 327

6. 517 – 196
7. 700 – 123
8. 1006 – 693
9. 3010 – 1015
10. 5500 – 750

11. 428 – 165
12. 684 – 338
13. 472 – 195
14. 740 – 174
15. 603 – 136

16. 1416 – 878
17. 3463 – 1685
18. 7500 – 5673
19. 7070 – 2475
20. 6003 – 2748

21. Subtract 183 from 420

22. What is the difference between 640 and 64?

23. What must be added to 420 to make 1100?

24. From 753 take 587

25. How many less is 79 than 97?

26. Take 1243 from 5138

27. What must be subtracted from 950 to leave 672?

28. How many more is 1250 than 675?

29. From 1000 subtract 296

30. What is 7000 minus 2483?

End of chapter activity: Magic squares revisited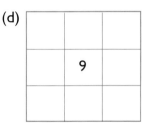

In a magic square, each line (vertical, horizontal and diagonal) adds up to the same total.

In this example the total is 15

8	1	6
3	5	7
4	9	2

Copy and complete these magic squares

(a)

9	2	7
4	6	8
5	10	3

(b)

10		8
	7	
		4

(c)

11		9
7		5

(d)

	9	

Can you make a 3 x 3 magic square where the total of each line is 36?

Tip: Look carefully at the magic squares you have already made. Can you see any patterns?

Did you know?

Cheetahs are the fastest mammals. They can reach speeds of 110 km/hour or 70 mph. If they went any faster they would be breaking the motorway limit.

Chapter 5: Addition and subtraction

In Chapter 3 we practised addition, and in Chapter 4 we reminded ourselves about subtraction. Now let us look at how to work out calculations which include both. The important thing to remember is that the **+** and **−** signs tell us what to do with the number that comes immediately **after** them.

Examples:

(i)   4 + 3   Start at 4 and add 3 to get the answer 7

(ii)   4 − 3   Start at 4 and subtract 3 to get the answer 1

(iii) 10 + 5 + 1   Start at 10, add 5 and then add 1 to get the answer 16

(iv) 10 + 5 − 1   Start at 10, add 5 and then subtract 1 to get the answer 14

(v)   10 − 5 + 1   Start at 10, subtract 5 and then add 1 to get the answer 6

(vi) 10 − 5 − 1   Start at 10, subtract 5 and then subtract 1 to get the answer 4

Exercise 5.1: Addition and subtraction

Calculate:

1. 65 + 27

2. 65 − 27

3. 74 + 43 + 19

4. 74 + 43 − 19

5. 74 − 43 + 19

6. 74 − 43 − 19

7. 69 + 107 − 87

8. 138 − 26 − 65

9. 240 − 159 + 28

10. 57 + 248 − 126

11. 486 − 193 − 76

12. 842 + 317 − 623

13. 300 − 129 + 87

14. 845 + 72 − 386

15. 729 − 436 − 109

16. 1260 + 970 − 780

17. 3100 − 1642 − 875

18. 4250 − 2376 + 1062

19. 376 + 4932 − 785

20. 2000 − 73 − 846

Inverses

Remember that addition and subtraction are the **opposite** of each other:

- Addition is the **inverse** of subtraction.

- Subtraction is the **inverse** of addition.

If you know that: 20 + 10 = 30
(Remember that 10 + 20 also equals 30)

then you also know that: 30 − 20 = 10

and that: 30 − 10 = 20

Exercise 5.2: Inverses

Copy these calculations and complete them by putting the missing number in the box.

1. 9 + 6 = ☐

2. 6 + 9 = ☐

3. 15 − 9 = ☐

4. 15 − 6 = ☐

5. 24 + 18 = ☐

6. ☐ + 24 = 42

7. 42 − ☐ = 24

8. ☐ − 24 = 18

9. 116 − ☐ = 64

10. ☐ + 64 = 116

11. $82 + \boxed{} = 204$

12. $138 - \boxed{} = 43$

13. $\boxed{} + 70 = 220$

14. $\boxed{} - 60 = 212$

15. $117 + 89 = \boxed{}$

16. $320 - 117 = \boxed{}$

17. $\boxed{} - 200 = 250$

18. $40 + \boxed{} = 340$

19. $\boxed{} - 85 = 185$

20. $\boxed{} + 85 = 185$

Problem solving

We often use addition and subtraction to solve word problems. Many questions can be answered using a single calculation, but it usually helps to think things through in steps.

Example:

Jean and Simone are picking apples for Farmer Brown. Jean picks 135 apples and Simone picks 180.

Then they take out 17 rotten apples. How many apples do they give to Farmer Brown?

They pick $135 + 180 = 315$ apples.

They take out the 17 rotten apples: $315 - 17 = 298$ apples.

They give Farmer Brown 298 apples.

We can write this as a single calculation: $135 + 180 - 17 = 298$

Exercise 5.3: Problem solving

1. There are 32 children at a picnic. 12 each have a packet of plain crisps and 7 each have a packet of flavoured crisps. How many children do not have crisps?

2. There are 96 tins of soup on the top shelf and a further 48 tins of soup on the bottom shelf. 27 tins of soup are sold. How many tins of soup are left?

3. Mrs Root has 19 exercise books left. She knows this will not be enough to last the term. She buys 72 more exercise books. During the term her form uses 58 of them.
How many exercise books are left at the end of term?

4. Matthew, Mark and Luke set out to sell 1000 raffle tickets in aid of the church roof fund. Matthew sells 346, Mark 481 and Luke 160

   (a) Do they reach their target?

   (b) How many over or short of the target are they?

5. Milkman Mike sets off with 600 pints of milk on his float. He delivers 132 pints at the school and 276 pints at the hospital. The rest are delivered to the corner shop. How many pints does Mike leave at the corner shop?

6. Tina starts a game of marbles with 70 marbles. She loses 17 to Freya but then captures 29 from Bella.
How many marbles does Tina have at the end?

7. Alison comes top in a verbal reasoning test, with 825 marks. Bottom of the class are Yves who gets 386 marks and Zebedee with 357 marks.
How many more marks does Alison get than the bottom two combined?

8. 1100 passengers board the Scottish Express in London. 147 get off the train at Birmingham but 119 get on.
How many passengers are there on the train when it leaves Birmingham?

9. In a maths test Henry gets 85% and Jeremy gets 48%. Sally notices that she scores 29 more than the difference between Henry's and Jeremy's scores.
What is Sally's percentage?

10. Vikram needs a total of 501 in 4 rounds of darts to win a prize. He scores 140, 135, 98 and 121
Does Vikram win the prize?

Exercise 5.4: Summary exercise

1. Calculate:

   (a) 37 + 46 − 25

   (b) 62 + 19 − 57

   (c) 154 − 87 + 33

   (d) 120 − 45 − 38

2. Copy these calculations and complete them by putting the missing number in the box:

   (a) 43 + 64 = ☐

   (b) 140 − 73 = ☐

   (c) ☐ − 80 = 145

   (d) ☐ + 80 = 145

   (e) 35 + 27 + ☐ = 110

   (f) 58 + ☐ − 46 = 80

   (g) ☐ − 12 − 38 = 25

   (h) 70 − 47 + ☐ = 60

   (i) 125 + 33 − ☐ = 68

   (j) 40 − 30 − ☐ = 0

End of chapter activity: A magic number

Here is a party trick you can use to impress your friends and family. Try it a few times yourself first, to see what happens.

- Write down a 3-digit number with decreasing digits (e.g. 321).

- Reverse the number and subtract it from the first number (e.g. 321 − 123 = 198).

- Take the answer and add it to its reverse (e.g. 198 + 891 = 1089).

What answer do you get?

Try this a few more times, starting with different digits. What do you notice about the answers?

Now you are ready to try your party trick on your friends!

Did you know?

At the last count there were 187 countries in the world.

Chapter 6: Multiplication

You probably know lots of different ways to multiply numbers together (have a look at Chapter 26: Mental strategies to remind you of some of the methods). In this chapter we are going to use these skills with larger numbers.

Multiples and tables

A times table lists the **multiples** of a number.

$3 \times 4 = 12$

12 is the **product** of 3 and 4

12 is the 4th **multiple** of 3

12 is the 3rd **multiple** of 4

You should already know your 2, 3, 4, 5, 6 and 10 times tables. Now you need to learn your 7, 8, 9, 11 and 12 times tables. Make sure you know them well before you attempt the exercises that follow.

7 times table

$1 \times 7 = 7$	
$2 \times 7 = 14$	
$3 \times 7 = 21$	
$4 \times 7 = 28$	
$5 \times 7 = 35$	
$6 \times 7 = 42$	
$7 \times 7 = 49$	
$8 \times 7 = 56$	
$9 \times 7 = 63$	
$10 \times 7 = 70$	
$11 \times 7 = 77$	
$12 \times 7 = 84$	

Remember that you can multiply numbers in any order and the answer will be the same (e.g. $2 \times 7 = 7 \times 2 = 14$).

So there is not much new to learn. You already know

2×7	4×7	6×7
3×7	5×7	10×7

8 times table

1 x 8 = 8
2 x 8 = 16
3 x 8 = 24
4 x 8 = 32
5 x 8 = 40
6 x 8 = 48
7 x 8 = 56
8 x 8 = 64
9 x 8 = 72
10 x 8 = 80
11 x 8 = 88
12 x 8 = 96

There are hints about the 8 times table in Chapter 26: Mental strategies page 290.

9 times table

1 x 9 = 9
2 x 9 = 18
3 x 9 = 27
4 x 9 = 36
5 x 9 = 45
6 x 9 = 54
7 x 9 = 63
8 x 9 = 72
9 x 9 = 81
10 x 9 = 90
11 x 9 = 99
12 x 9 = 108

There are hints about the 9 times table in Chapter 26: Mental strategies page 291.

11 times table

1 x 11 = 11
2 x 11 = 22
3 x 11 = 33
4 x 11 = 44
5 x 11 = 55
6 x 11 = 66
7 x 11 = 77
8 x 11 = 88
9 x 11 = 99
10 x 11 = 110
11 x 11 = 121
12 x 11 = 132

The 11 times table is made up of (10 times) + (1 times):

10 + 1 = 11

20 + 2 = 22

30 + 3 = 33 and so on.

12 times table

1 x 12 = 12
2 x 12 = 24
3 x 12 = 36
4 x 12 = 48
5 x 12 = 60
6 x 12 = 72
7 x 12 = 84
8 x 12 = 96
9 x 12 = 108
10 x 12 = 120
11 x 12 = 132
12 x 12 = 144

The 12 times table is made up of (10 times) + (2 times):

10 + 2 = 12

20 + 4 = 24

30 + 6 = 36 and so on.

Exercise 6.1: Multiples

Write down in which table will you find these multiples?

1.	6	9	12	15
2.	12	18	24	30
3.	18	27	36	45
4.	6	8	10	12
5.	12	16	20	24
6.	24	32	40	48
7.	48	60	72	84
8.	24	30	36	42

9.	99	110	121	132
10.	55	60	65	70
11.	72	80	88	96
12.	72	81	90	99
13.	25	50	75	100
14.	15	30	45	60
15.	60	80	100	120

Exercise 6.2: Tables Ⓕ

Write down the answers to the following. See how quickly can you answer these questions!

1. 3×8

2. 5×7

3. 9×11

4. 4×12

5. 6×9

6. two sevens

7. eleven elevens

8. five eights

9. four nines

10. eight twelves

11. 7 times 7

12. 9 times 9

13. 10 times 11

14. 6 times 8

15. 12 times 7

16. 8 multiplied by 8

17. 7 multiplied by 11

18. 6 multiplied by 12

19. 9 multiplied by 7

20. 11 multiplied by 8

21. the product of 12 and 9

22. the product of 6 and 7

23. the product of 8 and 4

24. the product of 11 and 12

25. the product of 9 and 5

26. the 6th multiple of 4

27. the 4th multiple of 6

28. the 12th multiple of 12

29. the 8th multiple of 9

30. the 3rd multiple of 11

Multiplying by 1000

You should already know that when we **multiply by 10**, the digits move **1 place to the left**. The **Units** digit moves to the **Tens** column.

Examples:

(i) $4 \times 10 = 40$
(ii) $65 \times 10 = 650$
(iii) $450 \times 10 = 4500$

You should also know that when we **multiply by 100**, the digits move **2 places to the left**. The **Units** digit moves to the **Hundreds** column.

Examples:

(i) $3 \times 100 = 300$
(ii) $27 \times 100 = 2700$
(iii) $250 \times 100 = 25\ 000$

Can you guess what happens when we multiply by 1000?

When we **multiply by 1000**, the digits move **3 places to the left**. The **Units** digit moves to the **Thousands** column.

Examples:

(i) $7 \times 1000 = 7000$
(ii) $34 \times 1000 = 34\ 000$
(iii) $460 \times 1000 = 460\ 000$

Exercise 6.3: Multiples of 10, 100 and 1000

Calculate the following:

1. 5 × 10
2. 135 × 10
3. 83 × 10
4. 4000 × 10
5. 310 × 10

6. 819 × 100
7. 5000 × 100
8. 75 × 100
9. 3450 × 100
10. 5 × 100

11. 25 × 1000
12. 1780 × 1000
13. 20 000 × 1000
14. 382 × 1000
15. 8 × 1000

16. 5000 × 1000
17. 700 × 1000
18. 6575 × 1000
19. 60 × 1000
20. 1000 × 1000

· ·

Square numbers

Square numbers are a special group of numbers which can be drawn as squares.

1, 4 and 9 are the smallest square numbers. Use Exercise 6.4 to find some more.

Exercise 6.4: Square numbers

1. Take a piece of squared paper and see how many other square numbers you can draw, up to 100

2. Can you explain what a square number is? Write down your explanation.

The square numbers up to 100 are:

1	(1 × 1)
4	(2 × 2)
9	(3 × 3)
16	(4 × 4)
25	(5 × 5)
36	(6 × 6)
49	(7 × 7)
64	(8 × 8)
81	(9 × 9)
100	(10 × 10)

×	1	2	3	4	5	6	7	8	9	10
1	1	2	3	4	5	6	7	8	9	10
2	2	4	6	8	10	12	14	16	18	20
3	3	6	9	12	15	18	21	24	27	30
4	4	8	12	16	20	24	28	32	36	40
5	5	10	15	20	25	30	35	40	45	50
6	6	12	18	24	30	36	42	48	54	60
7	7	14	21	28	35	42	49	56	63	70
8	8	16	24	32	40	48	56	64	72	80
9	9	18	27	36	45	54	63	72	81	90
10	10	20	30	40	50	60	70	80	90	100

Square numbers are the result of multiplying a number by itself. On a multiplication square, they form a diagonal line from top left to bottom right.

You should learn the list of square numbers. They are just special multiples that you know already.

Multiplying a 2-digit number by a 1-digit number

Multiplication by partition

Partition means separation. We can make multiplications simpler by partitioning one of the numbers.

Example: $67 \times 8 = (60 \times 8) + (7 \times 8)$

$= 480 + 56$

$= 536$

Think of 67 as 60 + 7 and multiply each part by 8

Exercise 6.5: Multiplication by partition

Calculate the following using partition:

1. 38×2
2. 49×3
3. 86×4
4. 91×5
5. 65×6

6. 74×7
7. 28×8
8. 17×9
9. 81×7
10. 57×4

11. 59×6
12. 36×9
13. 43×7
14. 87×2
15. 71×5

16. 97×8
17. 83×3
18. 27×9
19. 67×7
20. 54×4

The formal method of multiplication

Like the formal methods of addition and subtraction, the formal method of multiplication involves writing the numbers in place value columns. You can then multiply each column in turn.

Example: 67 x 8

H	T	U
	6	7
x		8
	5	6
+ 4	8	0
	5	3	6

First 7 x 8 = 56

Then 60 x 8 = 480

Now add the answers together 56 + 480 = 536

Exercise 6.6: The formal method of multiplication (1)

Calculate the following using the formal method:

1.   24 x 7
2.   47 x 5
3.   79 x 2
4.   16 x 7

5.   68 x 8
6.   52 x 3
7.   38 x 9
8.   83 x 8

9.   97 x 4
10. 19 x 6
11. 27 x 3
12. 42 x 6

This formal method can be make quicker by using a **carrying figure**, like we did in addition.

Example: 67 x 8

H	T	U
	6	7
x		8
5	3	6
	5	

First 7 x 8 = 56 so write 6 in the answer row and carry the 5 into the **Tens** column

Then multiply 6 x 8 = 48, and don't forget to add the carried 5 to give 53

Exercise 6.7: The formal method of multiplication (2)

Calculate the following using the formal method, carrying where necessary:

1.

	H	T	U
		2	9
×			6

2.

		H	T	U
			4	6
×				3

3

		H	T	U
			7	8
×				5

4. 65 × 8

5. 37 × 4

6. 52 × 6

7. 93 × 2

8. 81 × 7

9. 14 × 9

10. 84 × 3

11. 47 × 7

12. 61 × 9

13. 56 × 6

14. 75 × 5

15. 98 × 2

16. 34 × 9

17. 23 × 4

18. 15 × 8

19. 59 × 7

20. 38 × 3

Multiplying a 3-digit number by a 1-digit number

We multiply a 3-digit number in exactly the same way as a 2-digit number. There is just one extra step.

Example:	376 × 8	
Partition:	376 × 8 = (300 × 8) + (70 × 8) + (6 × 8)	Think of 376 as 300 + 70 + 6 and multiply each part by 8
	= 2400 + 560 + 48	
	= 3008	

Formal method:

Th	H	T	U
	3	7	6
×			8
		4	8
	5	6	0
2	4	0	0
3	0	0	8

Step 1: 6 x 8 = 48

Step 2: 70 x 8 = 560

Step 3: 300 x 8 = 2400

Finally add 48 + 560 + 2400 = 3008

Formal method, using carrying:

Th	H	T	U
	3	7	6
×			8
3	0	0	8
		6	4

Step 1: 6 x 8 = 48 so write 8 in the answer row and carry the 4

Step 2: 7 x 8 = 56, plus the carried 4 is 60, so write 0 in the answer row and carry the 6

Step 3: 3 x 8 = 24, plus the carried 6 gives 30

Exercise 6.8: Further multiplication

Calculate the following using an appropriate method:

1. 267 x 2

2. 136 x 8

3. 429 x 5

4. 742 x 6

5. 148 x 9

6. 236 x 3

7. 814 x 7

8. 729 x 4

9. 164 x 8

10. 425 x 6

11. 853 x 4

12. 729 x 3

13. 375 x 7

14. 591 x 5

15. 984 x 2

16. 720 x 8

17. 407 x 9

18. 714 x 6

19. 836 x 3

20. 909 x 5

Problem solving

Multiplication problems often involve finding the number of items in several containers (boxes, packets, etc). This is a very useful skill for everyday life.

Exercise 6.9: Problem solving Finn ✓ 12-08-17

1. Tennis balls are sold in boxes of six.
    The Tennis Club orders 48 boxes.
    How many tennis balls have been ordered?

2. Notebooks are packed in parcels of 24
    Seven parcels are delivered. How many
    notebooks are there altogether in the
    parcels?

3. A tray contains 36 eggs. During the day
    Mary collects enough eggs to fill nine trays
    exactly. How many eggs does Mary collect
    during the day?

4. There are 48 cans of fizzy drink in a plastic carton. The corner shop
    takes delivery of eight cartons. How many cans of fizzy drink have been
    delivered?

5. You can buy stamps in booklets of 12.
    How many stamps are there in 25 booklets?

6. A carpenter wants to order a supply of screws which are sold in
    boxes of 144.
    He orders five boxes. How many screws does the carpenter order?

7. At the beginning of term, all 185 children are given three pencils each.
    What is the total number of pencils handed out at the beginning
    of term?

8. During a season of motor races,
    Manuel changes all four tyres on his
    car 124 times altogether. How many
    tyres does he use during the season?

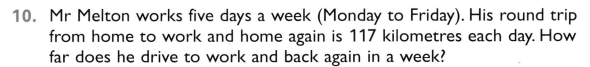

9. An average adult elephant will eat 205 kilograms of vegetation each day. How much would you expect it to eat in a week (seven days)?

10. Mr Melton works five days a week (Monday to Friday). His round trip from home to work and home again is 117 kilometres each day. How far does he drive to work and back again in a week?

. . . .

Exercise 6.10: Summary exercise

1. Calculate the following:

   (a) 4 × 7
   (b) 9 × 3
   (c) 11 × 6
   (d) 5 × 12
   (e) 8 × 7

   (f) the 4th multiple of 9
   (g) eleven times 4
   (h) seven threes
   (i) the product of 10 and 10
   (j) the square numbers less than 50

2. Calculate the following:

   (a) 87 × 10
   (b) 2396 × 1000
   (c) 8 × 100
   (d) 45 × 1000
   (e) 567 × 100

   (f) 10 × 1000
   (g) 6900 × 10
   (h) 650 × 1000
   (i) 40 × 100
   (j) 75 000 × 1000

3. Calculate the following using the formal method:

   (a) 74 × 2
   (b) 26 × 4
   (c) 96 × 5
   (d) 15 × 8
   (e) 67 × 6

   (f) 85 × 3
   (g) 39 × 7
   (h) 42 × 9
   (i) 53 × 8
   (j) 93 × 6

(k) 56 × 4   (p) 624 × 3

(l) 84 × 7   (q) 157 × 2

(m) 39 × 6   (r) 623 × 4

(n) 53 × 9   (s) 260 × 7

(o) 86 × 5   (t) 105 × 9

End of chapter activity: Another way to multiply

This is a method used by an American boy.

Multiply 23 × 5

Step 1: Draw up a grid with the numbers outside it.

Step 2: Work out 2 × 5 and 3 × 5 and write the answers in the squares as shown.

2 × 5 = 10 and 3 × 5 = 15

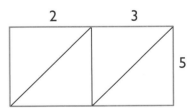

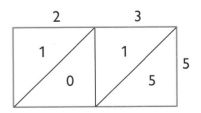

Step 3: Add diagonally, starting on the right

23 x 5 = 115

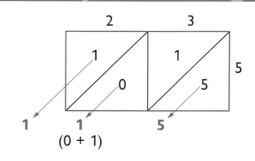

Here are some more examples.

27 x 3

Note: 2 x 3 = 6 is written as 06

27 x 3 = 81

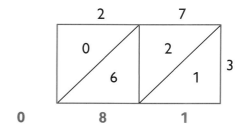

78 x 8

Note: 6 + 6 = 12, so write down 2 and carry the 1

78 x 8 = 624

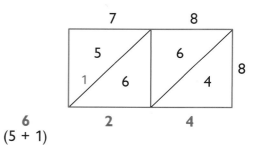

375 x 9

375 x 9 = 3375

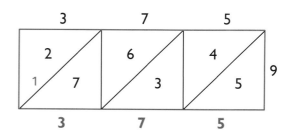

Work out these using the American method:

1. 47 x 6

2. 75 x 7

3. 69 x 8

4. 143 x 5

5. 426 x 4

6. 296 x 9

Now make up some for yourself.

Did you know?

The Channel Tunnel between England and France is the longest undersea tunnel in the world. It is **37.9** kilometres, or **23.55** miles, long.

Chapter 7: Division

So far in this book we have learnt about addition, subtraction and multiplication, so now it is time to look at division. Remember, you can have a look at Chapter 26: Mental strategies if you want to remind yourself of some ways to divide in your head.

Division is the **inverse** (opposite) of multiplication. If you know that 6 x 7 is 42, you also know that 42 ÷ 6 = 7 and 42 ÷ 7 = 6

Can you remember your 7, 8, 9, 11 and 12 times tables? If you need to remind yourself go back to pages 48–50. You are going to use them in this exercise.

Exercise 7.1: Easy division

1. Divide:
    (a) 18 by 9
    (b) 21 by 7
    (c) 36 by 12
    (d) 24 by 8
    (e) 55 by 11
    (f) 80 by 8
    (g) 72 by 9
    (h) 60 by 12
    (i) 88 by 11
    (j) 42 by 7

2. Share:
    (a) 48 among 12
    (b) 48 among 8
    (c) 56 among 7
    (d) 110 among 11
    (e) 36 among 9
    (f) 64 among 8
    (g) 49 among 7
    (h) 108 among 12
    (i) 54 among 9
    (j) 132 among 11

3. Work out:
    (a) how many sevens there are in 63
    (b) how many elevens there are in 121
    (c) how many nines there are in 81
    (d) how many twelves there are in 144
    (e) how many eights there are in 96

4. Calculate:

    (a) $\frac{1}{8}$ of 16   (f) an eighth of 40

    (b) $\frac{1}{7}$ of 28   (g) $\frac{1}{12}$ of 84

    (c) a ninth of 45   (h) $\frac{1}{9}$ of 27

    (d) a twelfth of 24   (i) a seventh of 35

    (e) $\frac{1}{11}$ of 77   (j) an eleventh of 22

5. Sometimes the answer to a division is not exact; there is something left over, a **remainder**. In this question remember to write down the answer and any remainder.

    Calculate the following:

    (a) 44 ÷ 8   (f) 30 ÷ 9

    (b) 24 ÷ 9   (g) 30 ÷ 11

    (c) 110 ÷ 12   (h) 30 ÷ 8

    (d) 74 ÷ 7   (i) 30 ÷ 12

    (e) 122 ÷ 11   (j) 30 ÷ 7

Dividing by 1000

You should already know that when we **divide by 10**, the digits move **1 place to the right**. The **Tens** digit moves to the **Units** column.

Examples:

(i)   60 ÷ 10 = 6

(ii)   470 ÷ 10 = 47

(iii) 2000 ÷ 10 = 200

You should also know that when we **divide by 100**, the digits move **2 places to the right**. The **Hundreds** digit moves to the **Units** column.

Examples:

(i)   800 ÷ 100 = **8**

(ii) 3500 ÷ 100 = **35**

(iii) 75 **000** ÷ 100 = 75**0**

Can you guess what happens when we divide by 1000?

When we **divide by 1000**, the digits move **3 places to the right**. The **Thousands** digit moves to the **Units** column.

Examples:

(i)   9000 ÷ 1000 = **9**

(ii) 17 000 ÷ 1000 = **17**

(iii) 750 **000** ÷ 1000 = 75**0**

Exercise 7.2: Division by 10, 100 and 1000

Calculate the following:

1. 80 ÷ 10
2. 500 ÷ 10
3. 420 ÷ 10
4. 4300 ÷ 10
5. 8680 ÷ 10

6. 400 ÷ 100
7. 1900 ÷ 100
8. 54 700 ÷ 100
9. 40 000 ÷ 100
10. 900 000 ÷ 100

11. 5000 ÷ 1000
12. 96 000 ÷ 1000
13. 482 000 ÷ 1000
14. 320 000 ÷ 1000
15. 900 000 ÷ 1000

16. 30 000 ÷ 1000
17. 8000 ÷ 1000
18. 62 000 ÷ 1000
19. 450 000 ÷ 1000
20. 610 000 ÷ 1000

Informal division

You can think of division as repeated subtraction. You can calculate a division by subtracting the same number until you can't go any further.

Example: 15 ÷ 5

How many times can we subtract 5 from 15?

H	T	U	
	1	5	
−		5	**1** lot of 5
	1	0	
−		5	**1** lot of 5
		5	
−		5	**1** lot of 5
		0	

We can take 5 away 3 times. So there are 3 fives in 15

15 ÷ 5 = 3

When the numbers we are working with are larger, we need to subtract multiples of the **divisor** (the number we are dividing by).

Example: 68 ÷ 4

How many times can we subtract 4 from 68?

H	T	U	
	6	8	
−	4	0	**10** lots of 4
	2	8	
−	2	8	**7** lots of 4
	0	0	

We can take 4 away 10 + 7 = 17 times.

68 ÷ 4 = 17

Exercise 7.3: Informal division

Calculate the following, using an appropriate method (all answers are exact). Make sure you can explain how you got your answers.

1. 32 ÷ 2
2. 45 ÷ 3
3. 56 ÷ 4
4. 85 ÷ 5
5. 96 ÷ 6

6. 98 ÷ 7
7. 87 ÷ 3
8. 76 ÷ 2
9. 70 ÷ 5
10. 72 ÷ 4

11. 126 ÷ 2
12. 129 ÷ 3
13. 148 ÷ 4
14. 125 ÷ 5
15. 108 ÷ 6

16. 133 ÷ 7
17. 136 ÷ 8
18. 126 ÷ 9
19. 170 ÷ 10
20. 180 ÷ 12

The formal method of division

The formal method of division looks quite different from the formal methods of additions, subtraction and multiplication. However, we still look at each place value column in turn. Let's look at 68 ÷ 4 again.

Example: 68 ÷ 4

4	6	8

Step 1: Set the calculation out like this. Leave room to write the answer above.

	1	
4	6	²8

Step 2: Look at the first number, 6, first. 6 ÷ 4 = 1 remainder 2, so put 1 above the line and write the 2, which represents 20 units, next to the second number, 8

	1	7
4	6	²8

Step 3: Now look at the 8 and the carrying figure, 28 28 ÷ 4 = 7, so write 7 above the line.

So your answer is 68 ÷ 4 = 17

Using this method, you can do much of the working in your head. Here are some more examples.

Examples:

(i) 78 ÷ 3

		2	6	
	3	7	¹8	

7 ÷ 3 = 2 remainder 1, so write 2 above the line and carry the 1

18 ÷ 3 = 6, so write 6 above the line

78 ÷ 3 = 26

(ii) 735 ÷ 5

		1	4	7
	5	7	²3	³5

7 ÷ 5 = 1 remainder 2

23 ÷ 5 = 4 remainder 3

35 ÷ 5 = 7

735 ÷ 5 = 147

(iii) 438 ÷ 6

			7	3
	6	4	3	¹8

6 doesn't go into 4 so look at 43

43 ÷ 6 = 7 remainder 1

18 ÷ 6 = 3

438 ÷ 6 = 73

Exercise 7.4: The formal method of division

Calculate the following using the formal method (all answers are exact):

1.

	2	7	4

2.

	3	8	4

3.

	4	9	2

4. 65 ÷ 5

5. 84 ÷ 6

6. 91 ÷ 7

7. 58 ÷ 2

8. 42 ÷ 3

9. 68 ÷ 4

10. 108 ÷ 2

11. 156 ÷ 3   15. 168 ÷ 7   19. 174 ÷ 6

12. 136 ÷ 4   16. 120 ÷ 8   20. 184 ÷ 8

13. 135 ÷ 5   17. 126 ÷ 9

14. 138 ÷ 6   18. 160 ÷ 5

21. 536 ÷ 2   25. 954 ÷ 6   29. 935 ÷ 5

22. 741 ÷ 3   26. 861 ÷ 7   30. 861 ÷ 3

23. 788 ÷ 4   27. 912 ÷ 8

24. 575 ÷ 5   28. 792 ÷ 4

31. 176 ÷ 2   35. 342 ÷ 6   39. 540 ÷ 9

32. 260 ÷ 5   36. 375 ÷ 5   40. 832 ÷ 4

33. 294 ÷ 3   37. 296 ÷ 8

34. 441 ÷ 7   38. 329 ÷ 7

Checking your answers

You have already learnt that multiplication and division are the opposite of each other:

- **Multiplication** is the **inverse** of **division**
- **Division** is the **inverse** of **multiplication**

If you know that $18 \times 5 = 90$

then you also know that $5 \times 18 = 90$

and that $90 \div 5 = 18$

and that $90 \div 18 = 5$

If you know that $84 \div 3 = 28$

then you also know that $84 \div 28 = 3$

and that $28 \times 3 = 84$

and that $3 \times 28 = 84$

You can use this relationship to check your answers when you multiply or divide.

Examples:

(i) Is 45 x 6 = 270 correct?

Check by working out 270 ÷ 6

270 ÷ 6 = 45   So, yes it is correct.

(ii) Is 185 ÷ 5 = 37 correct?

Check by working out 37 x 5

37 x 5 = 185   So, yes it is correct.

Exercise 7.5: Checking your answers

Copy these calculations and complete them by putting the missing number in the box.

1. (a) 9 x 4 = ☐

   (b) ☐ ÷ 4 = 9

   (c) 36 ÷ 9 = ☐

   (d) 4 x ☐ = 36

2. (a) 48 ÷ 6 = ☐

   (b) ☐ x 6 = 48

   (c) ☐ ÷ 8 = 6

3. (a) 30 ÷ ☐ = 10

   (b) 10 x ☐ = 30

   (c) ☐ ÷ 10 = 3

4. (a) ☐ ÷ 8 = 5

   (b) 8 x ☐ = 40

5. ☐ x 4 = 20

6. ☐ ÷ 3 = 7

7. 2 x ☐ = 12

8. ☐ ÷ 10 = 8

9. 45 ÷ ☐ = 9

10. 7 x ☐ = 28

11. 12 x 4 = ☐

12. ☐ ÷ 4 = 16

Work out and write down whether these calculations are right or wrong:

13. (a) 14 x 3 = 42

(b) 18 x 4 = 82

(c) 26 x 5 = 130

(d) 34 x 7 = 238

(e) 26 x 6 = 146

(f) 21 x 9 = 189

(g) 20 x 10 = 201

(h) 42 x 8 = 336

(i) 53 x 9 = 477

(j) 101 x 2 = 220

(k) 48 ÷ 3 = 16

(l) 86 ÷ 4 = 24

(m) 114 ÷ 6 = 19

(n) 168 ÷ 7 = 24

(o) 144 ÷ 8 = 16

(p) 198 ÷ 9 = 22

(q) 216 ÷ 2 = 103

(r) 305 ÷ 7 = 45

(s) 176 ÷ 8 = 22

(t) 402 ÷ 2 = 21

Problem solving

Division problems often involve sharing a number of items between several containers or people, and so on. Sometimes you will need to think carefully about your answer.

Example:

Karen invites 20 friends to a party. She wants to give each guest a party hat.

The party hats are sold in packs of six. How many packs should Karen buy?

20 ÷ 6 = 3 remainder 2

If Karen buys 3 packs she won't have enough party hats, and she can't buy part of a pack.

So she must buy 4 packs of party hats.

Exercise 7.6: Problem solving

1. Four brothers divide a packet of 24 toffees equally among themselves. How many toffees does each brother get?

2. Mediaeval Mead is delivered in boxes of six bottles. The local store orders 84 bottles.
   How many boxes will be delivered?

3. Jenny, Katie and Lisa share a bowl of 54 cherries between them equally. How many cherries does Jenny eat?

4. A party of 12 people is going to the theatre. A taxi is allowed to carry only five passengers.
   How many taxis must be ordered to take the whole party to the theatre?

5. Jack picks 252 daffodils and divides them into seven equal bunches.
   How many daffodils are there in a bunch?

6. Form 6 starts the term with a box of 144 pencils in their classroom. At the end of term only $\frac{1}{9}$ of the pencils remain unused.
   How many pencils are left unused?

7. Eggs are packed in boxes of six.
   How many boxes are needed to pack 300 eggs?

8. A shooting team of 8 totals 768 points in a match. Very surprisingly each member of the team gets the same score.
   What is each member's score?

9. The four members of a polo team share the £900 winners' prize equally.
   How much does each player win?

10. A librarian arranges 168 books in piles of 12
    How many piles are there?

Exercise 7.7: Summary exercise

1. Write down the answers to the following:

   (a) 21 ÷ 3

   (b) 40 divided by 8

   (c) 54 shared equally between 6

   (d) How many elevens are there in 110?

   (e) How many are left over when 29 is divided by 12?

   (f) What is $\frac{1}{8}$ of 56?

2. Calculate the following:

   (a) 12 000 ÷ 1000

   (b) 1600 ÷ 10

   (c) 4000 ÷ 1000

   (d) 3500 ÷ 100

   (e) 800 000 ÷ 1000

3. Write down whether these calculations right or wrong.

   (a) 137 x 3 = 402

   (b) 182 ÷ 7 = 26

4. Calculate the following (all answers are exact):

   (a) 84 ÷ 6   (f) 586 ÷ 2

   (b) 116 ÷ 4   (g) 417 ÷ 3

   (c) 104 ÷ 8   (h) 387 ÷ 9

   (d) 265 ÷ 5   (i) 612 ÷ 6

   (e) 448 ÷ 7   (j) 560 ÷ 4

End of chapter activity: Yet another way to multiply

This method is often called Russian multiplication.

It involves **doubling** one number and **halving** another.

Example: 11 × 15

Step 1: Double and halve the numbers in two columns.

● Arrange your working in two columns

● Halve the numbers in the left-hand column and double the numbers in the right-hand column

● Ignore any remainders

● Stop when you get to 1 in the left-hand column

Halve this column / Double this column

1	1			1	5	

11 ÷ 2 (ignore remainder) → 5 → 3 0 ← 15 × 2 = 30
5 ÷ 2 (ignore remainer) → 2 → 6 0 ← 30 × 2 = 60
Stop when you reach 1 → 1 → 1 2 0

Step 2: Cross out all the even numbers in the left-hand column, and the numbers opposite them on the right.

1 1 | 1 5
5 | 3 0
First → 2 | 6 0 ← Then cross out number opposite 2
1 | 1 2 0

Step 3: Add the remaining numbers in the right-hand column to get the answer.

11 × 15 = 15 + 30 + 120 = 165

Check you can see how this example works.

Example: 36 × 8

3	6			8	
1	8			1	6
	9			3	2
	4			6	4
	2		1	2	8
	1		2	5	6

36 × 8 = 32 + 256 = 288

Remember that you can multiply numbers in any order, and the answer will be the same.

Example: 25 × 7   or   7 × 25

2	5			7	
1	2			1	4
	6			2	8
	3			5	6
	1		1	1	2

	7			2	5
	3			5	0
	1		1	0	0

25 × 7 = 7 + 56 + 112 = 175

7 × 25 = 25 + 50 + 100 = 175

This way round the working is shorter and there are no even numbers!

Calculate these using the Russian method:

1. 12 × 25

2. 11 × 23

3. 17 × 30

4. 32 × 15

5. 21 × 50

6. 13 × 22

Now make up some for yourself.

Did you know?

In the Houses of Parliament, a **division** is a vote in which MPs divide into two groups, one for the motion (Aye) and one against (No) the motion. A **division bell** is rung in the immediate neighbourhood of Parliament, even in local restaurants. Members have 8 minutes to reach the Aye or No **division lobby**.

Chapter 8: Functions

A **function** is like a machine that gives instructions about what to do with a number. We put a number in (the input), perform the function, and get a another number out (the output).

Finding outputs

To find an output, we simply have to follow the instructions the function gives us.

	Input	→	**Function**	→	**Output**	
(i)	4	→	add 3	→	?	4 + 3 = 7
(ii)	7	→	subtract 1	→	?	7 − 1 = 6
(iii)	5	→	multiply by 4	→	?	5 × 4 = 20
(iv)	18	→	divide by 6	→	?	18 ÷ 6 = 3

Examples:

We can write functions using words or symbols.

> **add 3** can be written as **+ 3**
> **subtract 1** can be written as **– 1**
> **multiply by 4** can be written as **x 4**
> **divide by 6** can be written as **÷ 6**

Exercise 8.1: Finding outputs (1)

Find the output for each of the following functions:

	Input	→	**Function**	→	**Output**
1.	9	→	+ 5	→	?
2.	8	→	− 4	→	?
3.	2	→	× 7	→	?
4.	24	→	÷ 6	→	?
5.	8	→	− 1	→	?

F. ✓

	Input	→	Function	→	Output
6.	12	→	÷ 2	→	?
7.	20	→	+ 6	→	?
8.	5	→	× 2	→	?
9.	7	→	− 3	→	?
10.	11	→	+ 8	→	?
11.	16	→	÷ 4	→	?
12.	9	→	+ 8	→	?
13.	28	→	− 9	→	?
14.	9	→	× 3	→	?
15.	20	→	÷ 10	→	?
16.	20	→	− 10	→	?
17.	3	→	+ 6	→	?
18.	6	→	÷ 3	→	?
19.	3	→	× 6	→	?
20.	6	→	− 3	→	?

Some functions tell you to carry out more than one operation on the input number.

Examples:

	Input	→	Function	→	Output	
(i)	19	→	− 3, ÷ 2	→	?	First 19 − 3 = 16 and then **16 ÷ 2 = 8**
(ii)	6	→	× 7, + 5	→	?	First 6 × 7 = 42 and then **42 + 5 = 47**
(iii)	30	→	÷ 5, × 4	→	?	First 30 ÷ 5 = 6 and then **6 × 4 = 24**

Exercise 8.2: Finding outputs (2)

Find the output for each of the following functions:

	Input	→	Function	→	Output
1.	9	→	+ 3, ÷ 6	→	?
2.	10	→	x 2, + 4	→	?
3.	17	→	− 5, x 2	→	?
4.	20	→	− 8, ÷ 3	→	?
5.	4	→	x 5, + 3	→	?
6.	11	→	− 6, x 3	→	?
7.	12	→	÷ 4, + 5	→	?
8.	30	→	− 2, ÷ 7	→	?
9.	40	→	÷ 4, x 3	→	?
10.	5	→	x 6, − 9	→	?
11.	28	→	÷ 7, + 5	→	?
12.	15	→	x 2, ÷ 3	→	?
13.	23	→	+ 2, x 2	→	?
14.	28	→	− 3, x 4	→	?
15.	15	→	+ 5, x 5	→	?

Use the next exercise to make sure you can also find outputs when the functions are written using words.

Exercise 8.3: Finding outputs using words

What is the answer if you:

1. think of 9 and add 4;

2. think of 23 and subtract 8;

3. think of 7 and multiply it by 6;

4. think of 33 and divide it by 3;

5. think of 10 and take 5 from it;

6. think of 7, add 3 and then multiply by 5;

7. think of 10, add 8 and then divide by 9;

8. think of 21, subtract 7 and then double the answer;

9. think of 40, take 4 away and then divide by 9;

10. think of 3, multiply by 5 and add 2 to the result;

11. think of 7, multiply by 4 and then subtract 18;

12. think of 12, divide by 3 and then add 4;

13. think of 36, divide by 9 and multiply the result by 3;

14. think of 45, subtract 15 from it and then divide by 5;

15. think of 50, divide it by 5 and multiply by 20?

Finding inputs

Can you solve these puzzles?

(i) Charlie thinks of a number, adds 4 and says his answer is 9
What number does Charlie think of?

(ii) Penny thinks of a number, subtracts 5 and says her answer is 7
What number does Penny think of?

(iii) Anurag thinks of a number, multiplies it by 4 and says his answer is 8
What number does Anurag think of?

(iv) Carla thinks of a number, divides it by 3 and says her answer is 10
What number does Carla think of?

When you were solving the puzzles, did you realise that you were solving a **function** question backwards?

You were given the **output** and had to find the **input**. To do this you found the **inverse function**.

You can write the inverse calculations from right to left (instead of from left to right, as usual).

		Input	→	Function	→	Output	Input	←	Inverse Function	←	Output
(i)	Charlie	?	→	+ 4	→	9	5	←	− 4	←	9
(ii)	Penny	?	→	− 5	→	7	12	←	+ 5	←	7
(iii)	Anurag	?	→	x 4	→	8	2	←	÷ 4	←	8
(iv)	Carla	?	→	÷ 3	→	10	30	←	x 3	←	10

- -

Exercise 8.4: Finding inputs

1. Find the input for each of the following functions:

	Input	→	Function	→	Output		Input	→	Function	→	Output
(a)	?	→	+ 3	→	11	(f)	?	→	x 6	→	30
(b)	?	→	− 6	→	26	(g)	?	→	+ 3	→	12
(c)	?	→	x 4	→	32	(h)	?	→	÷ 3	→	12
(d)	?	→	÷ 5	→	3	(i)	?	→	− 3	→	12
(e)	?	→	− 4	→	3	(j)	?	→	x 3	→	12

2. What number does Peter think of if he:

   (a) multiplies it by 7 and gets an answer of 21;

   (b) adds 12 to give a total of 23;

   (c) subtracts 9 and ends up with 12;

   (d) divides by 4 to get an answer of 12;

   (e) doubles it to get 50;

   (f) subtracts 10 to get an answer of 10;

   (g) multiplies by 2 to get an answer of 20;

   (h) adds 2 to get a total of 20;

   (i) halves it and ends up with 20;

   (j) takes 2 away and is left with 20?

Exercise 8.5: Summary exercise

1. Find the output for each of the following functions:

	Input	→	Function	→	Output
(a)	7	→	× 5	→	?
(b)	23	→	− 8	→	?
(c)	60	→	÷ 12	→	?
(d)	13	→	+ 37	→	?
(e)	36	→	÷ 3, + 15	→	?
(f)	3	→	× 7, − 17	→	?

2. What is the answer if you:

   (a) think of 9 and multiply it by 12;

   (b) think of 28 and subtract 12 from it before halving the answer?

3. Write down the input when it:

   (a) is divided by 2 to give an answer of 8;

   (b) is multiplied by 7 to give an answer of 56;

   (c) has 14 subtracted from it to give an answer of 20;

   (d) is added to 14 to give an answer of 20

4. (a) Alice thinks of a number and divides it by 9 to give an answer of 7
       What number did she think of?

   (b) Peter picks a number to which he adds 13
       He says his answer is 27. What number did Peter pick?

   (c) Louise subtracts 19 from a number and says she has a answer of 30
       What number did she start with?

   (d) Sandy multiplies a number by 8 to give him a total of 32
       What number did he start with?

End of chapter activity: Missing digits (addition)

These calculations are **additions**. An asterisk (*) represents a missing digit.

Re-write the sums without any digits missing.

1.

```
    3 4
  + 2 *
    * 7
```

2.

```
    6 *
  + * 5
    8 8
```

3.

```
    4 7
  + 2 5
    * 2
```

4.

```
    1 *
  + * 8
    5 6
```

5.

```
      * 4
  +   4 9
    * 2 3
```

6.

```
      5 6
  +   * *
    * 0 1
```

7.

```
    1 * 6
  +   6 *
    * 9 8
```

8.

```
    2 1 7
  +   * *
    * 6 4
```

9.

```
    3 * *
  + * 7 4
    8 1 6
```

10.

```
      4 * 3
  +   9 3 *
    * * 0 0
```

Did you know?

There are **646** members of Parliament. Each represents a constituency.

Constituency boundaries are reviewed every 10 or 15 years, so the total number does vary.

The largest constituency is the Isle of Wight with an electorate of about 110 000

The smallest constituency is Orkney and Shetland with an electorate of about 35 000

Chapter 9: Inequalities

We are used to saying, or writing, that numbers are **equal**.

We use the equals sign **=** to show that the value of each side of the sign is the same or equal.

Examples:

(i)　6 + 3 = 9

(ii)　5 = 7 − 2

(iii)　6 × 4 = 24

(iv)　5 = 15 ÷ 3

(v)　2 + 3 = 9 − 4

　　and so on.

Numbers can also be **compared** with each other.

Examples:

(i)　6 is larger than 2

(ii)　3 is smaller than 7

We can replace the words with signs:

- 　> means **is larger than / greater than**

- 　< means **is smaller than / less than**

Examples:

(i)　6 > 2　　　　This means 6 is larger than 2

(ii)　3 < 7　　　　This means 3 is less than 7

Use one of these hints to help you remember which sign is which.

• The open end faces the larger number.

• A crocodile opens its jaws wide to grab its food which gets smaller as it is digested.

• In music > means diminuendo
    (start loudly and become quieter)

and   < means crescendo (start quietly and become louder).

Exercise 9.1 : Inequality signs

1. Write the following in words:
    (a) 7 < 10
    (b) 8 > 2
    (c) 9 + 1 = 12 − 2
    (d) 5 > 1
    (e) 10 x 2 < 6 x 4

2. Use either >, < or = to compare the following:
    (a) 15   18   (f) 5 x 2   20 ÷ 4
    (b) 16   14   (g) 9 − 4   6 + 5
    (c) 51   15   (h) 8 x 2   20 − 16
    (d) 20   21   (i) 20 ÷ 4   4 + 1
    (e) 32   23   (j) 11 − 6   30 ÷ 3

    (k) 17 − 3   10 + 5   (n) $\frac{1}{4}$ of 80 $\frac{1}{2}$ of 100
    (l) 2 x 3   10 ÷ 5   (o) 12 ÷ 3   1 + 2 + 3
    (m) 7 x 3   3 x 7

End of chapter activity: Missing digits (subtraction)

These calculations are **subtractions**. An asterisk (*) represents a missing digit.

Re-write the sums without any digits missing.

1.

	*	6
−	7	*
	2	5

2.

	8	3
−	5	*
	2	9

3.

	7	4
−	3	*
	*	5

4.

	6	*
−	1	7
	*	3

5.

	7	4
−	*	*
	4	9

6.

	*	*
−	3	8
	2	5

7.

	6	*	7
−	*	4	5
	3	6	*

8.

	*	3	*
−	2	*	4
	2	1	7

9.

	*	*	*
−	2	1	9
	6	3	5

10.

	8	4	1
−	*	*	*
	6	4	5

Did you know?

The river Nile is generally regarded as the longest river in the world.

It is 6650 kilometres (4135 miles) long. This is the same as the distance from London to New Delhi, the capital of India.

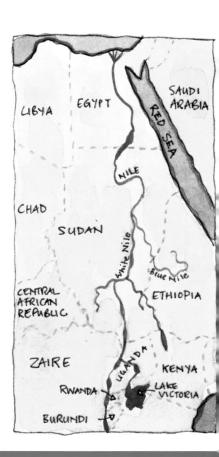

Chapter 10: Negative numbers

So far you have worked only with numbers that are greater than 0   >0

There are also numbers that are less than 0   <0

These are called **negative numbers**.

You may have met negative numbers already, in everyday life. For example, on a cold day, the **temperature** (on the Celsius scale) can be below zero (freezing).

Example:

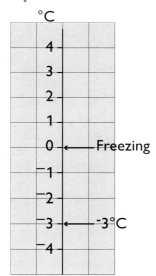

A temperature of ⁻3 °C is read as '**negative three degrees**' or '**minus** three degrees'.

Tip: Notice the position of the ⁻ sign. It looks like a subtraction sign (–) but is higher (⁻).

Look at this number line. It shows the numbers from ⁻5 to 5

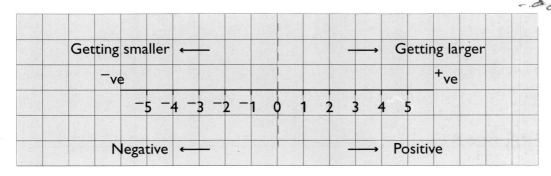

You can see from the number line that as you move in a **positive** direction (to the right), the numbers become **larger**:

- 5 is larger than 1 $5 > 1$
- 1 is larger than $^-4$ $1 > {}^-4$
- $^-1$ is larger than $^-4$ $^-1 > {}^-4$
- $^-3$ is larger than $^-7$ $^-3 > {}^-7$
- 0 is larger than $^-1$ $0 > {}^-1$

Tip: This can be difficult to understand when both the numbers are negative. Think of it in terms of having, or owing, money:

- Having £5 is better than having £1 $5 > 1$
- Having £1 is better than owing £4 $1 > {}^-4$
- Owing £1 is better than owing £4 $^-1 > {}^-4$
- Owing £3 is better than owing £7 $^-3 > {}^-7$
- Having no money is better than owing £1 $0 > {}^-1$

As you move in a **negative** direction (to the left), the numbers become **smaller**:

- 2 is smaller than 4 $2 < 4$
- $^-1$ is smaller than 3 $^-1 < 3$
- $^-3$ is smaller than $^-1$ $^-3 < {}^-1$
- $^-7$ is smaller than $^-6$ $^-7 < {}^-6$
- $^-4$ is smaller than 0 $^-4 < 0$

Tip: Again, when the numbers are both negative, it helps to think in terms of money:

- Having £2 is worse than having £4 $2 < 4$
- Having £1 is worse than having £3 $^-1 < 3$
- Owing £3 is worse than owing £1 $^-3 < {}^-1$
- Owing £7 is worse than owing £6 $^-7 < {}^-6$
- Owing £4 is worse than having no money $^-4 < 0$

Exercise 10.1: Ordering positive and negative numbers.

Use this number line to help you answer the questions.

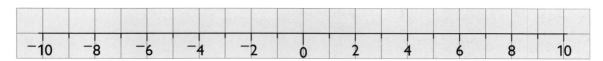

1. Write either 'is greater than' or 'is less than' to connect these numbers:

   (a) 4   7   (f) 9   7

   (b) ⁻4   ⁻8   (g) 9   ⁻7

   (c) ⁻1   ⁻6   (h) ⁻7   9

   (d) 5   ⁻2   (i) 7   9

   (e) 0   ⁻8   (j) ⁻7   ⁻9

2. Write either < or > to connect these numbers:

   (a) ⁻2   0   (f) ⁻7   ⁻3

   (b) 4   ⁻2   (g) 3   7

   (c) ⁻3   ⁻5   (h) ⁻7   3

   (d) ⁻4   ⁻1   (i) ⁻3   ⁻7

   (e) 8   ⁻8   (j) 7   ⁻3

3. Are the following statements true or false?

   (a) 6 > ⁻5   (e) ⁻5 < 6

   (b) ⁻6 > ⁻5   (f)   6 > 5

   (c) 5 < ⁻6   (g) ⁻6 > 5

   (d) 5 < 6   (h) ⁻5 < ⁻6

4. Write these numbers in order of size, starting with the **smallest**:

   (a) 3   4   ⁻2

   (b) ⁻7   7   6

   (c) ⁻4   ⁻5   4

   (d) 2   ⁻2   0

   (e) ⁻1   ⁻6   ⁻3

   (f) 5   6   1   2

   (g) ⁻5   ⁻6   ⁻1   ⁻2

   (h) ⁻8   4   1   ⁻1

   (i) ⁻1   1   0   2

   (j) 0   ⁻2   ⁻1   2

5. Write these numbers in order of size, starting with the **largest**:

   (a) 5   ⁻3   2

   (b) ⁻8   ⁻1   ⁻6

   (c) 3   5   ⁻4

   (d) ⁻1   0   1

   (e) ⁻2   ⁻4   4

   (f) 1   7   4   2

   (g) ⁻1   ⁻7   ⁻4   ⁻2

   (h) 5   ⁻7   8   ⁻6

   (i) 4   0   9   ⁻8

   (j) ⁻2   2   ⁻1   1

Negative numbers in real-life contexts

Look at this example of negative numbers.

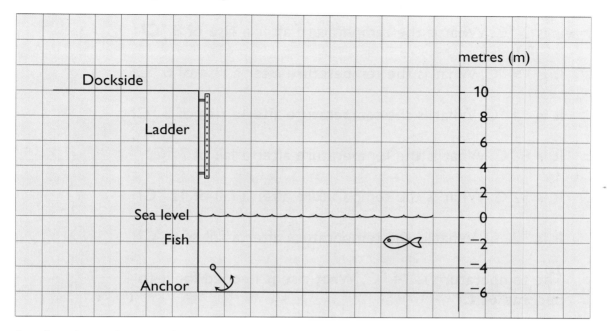

Sea level is taken as 0

Distances are measured above and below sea level:

- the dockside is at $^+10$, or 10 m **above** sea level
- the foot of the ladder is at $^+3$, or 3 m **above** sea level
- sea level is at 0
- the fish is at $^-2$, or 2 m **below** sea level
- the bottom of the anchor is at $^-6$, or 6 m **below** sea level

It follows that:

- the foot of the ladder is 7 m below the dockside

   $10 - 3 = 7$ This is the same as the length of the ladder.

- the fish is 4 m above the bottom of the anchor

   $6 - 2 = 4$ Both numbers are negative so you can ignore the signs.

- the anchor is 16 m below the dockside

   $10 + 6 = 16$ Add the 10 m above sea level and the 6 m below.

Exercise 10.2: Temperature changes f✓ 16/9/17

Use the thermometer on the right to help you answer the questions.

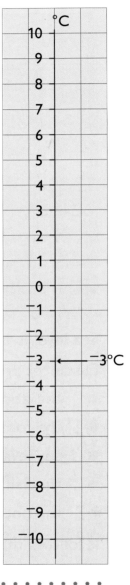

1. It is 2 °C. What is the temperature after a rise of 8 °C?

2. It is ⁻9 °C. What is the temperature after a rise of 6 °C?

3. It is ⁻1 °C. What is the temperature after a rise of 5 °C?

4. It is 8 °C. What is the temperature after a fall of 7 °C?

5. It is 5 °C. What is the temperature after a fall of 12 °C?

6. It is ⁻2 °C. What is the temperature after a fall of 6 °C?

7. The temperature is ⁻4 °C. What rise is needed for it to become 6 °C?

8. The temperature is ⁻2 °C. What fall is needed for it to become ⁻8 °C?

9. What is the fall in temperature when it goes from 10 °C to ⁻1 °C?

10. What rise in temperature is needed to go from ⁻6 °C to 8 °C?

. . . .

Exercise 10.3: Summary exercise f✓ 16/9/17

1. Write either 'is greater than' or 'is less than' to connect these numbers:

    (a) 3   ⁻6   (c) ⁻5   ⁻4

    (b) ⁻3   6   (d) ⁻1   ⁻7

2. Write either < or > to connect these numbers:

(a) ⁻2   0   (c) ⁻4   ⁻1

(b) 6   ⁻3   (d) ⁻6   ⁻8

3. Write these numbers in order of size, starting with the **largest**:

(a) ⁻2   0   ⁻6   1

(b) ⁻8   ⁻2   3   ⁻4

4. Write these numbers in order of size, starting with the **smallest**:

(a) ⁻1   ⁻4   3   ⁻6

(b) ⁻4   3   ⁻2   1

5. The temperature in London one day is 2 °C. In Helsinki it is ⁻15 °C. How much colder is it in Helsinki than in London?

6. It is 12 °C warmer in Kiev than in Moscow. What is the temperature in Kiev if it is ⁻5 °C in Moscow?

. . . .

End of chapter activity: Missing digits (multiplication)

These calculations are **multiplications**. An asterisk (*) represents a missing digit.

Re-write the sums without any digits missing.

1.

	*	3
×		4
	9	*

3.

	*	7
×		2
	7	*

2.

	*	7
×		*
	8	1

4.

	3	*
×		6
*	0	4

5.

	*	6
×		7
*	9	2

6.

	2	*
×		5
*	4	0

7.

	*	9
×		*
3	*	2

8.

	*	1
×		9
5	4	*

9.

	*	*
×		8
5	8	4

10.

	*	9
×		*
4	8	3

Did you know?

The **highest** point on the Earth's surface is the summit of Mount Everest at 8848 metres (29 028 feet) above sea level.

The **lowest** point on dry land is on the shores of the Dead Sea at 418 metres (1372 feet) below sea level.

Summit of Everest	+8848 metres
Sea level	0 metres
Dead Sea	⁻418 metres

Chapter 11: Sequences

A sequence is a series of patterns or numbers which are formed following a rule.

You should already have met some simple sequences, and know how to continue them.

Examples:

(i)

Rule: Add another row and column (the dots are arranged in squares: 1 x 1, 2 x 2, 3 x 3, 4 x 4, …)

The next two patterns are 5 x 5 and 6 x 6

(ii) 1   3   5   7

Rule: Add 2 (these are the odd numbers)

The next two terms (numbers) are 9 and 11

Exercise 11.1: Sequences

1. Copy the following sequences and add the next two patterns in each:

    (a)

    (b)

(c)

(d)

(e)

2. For each of these sequences:

(i) Write down the rule; and (ii) Write down the next two terms:

(a) 13   15   17   19   ☐ ☐

(b) 19   16   13   10   ☐ ☐

(c) 14   21   28   35   ☐ ☐

(d) 72   60   48   36   ☐ ☐

(e) 100 000   10 000   1000   100   ☐ ☐

(f) $^-5$ $^-3$ $^-1$ 1   ☐ ☐

(g) 8   6   4   2   ☐ ☐

(h) 16   11   6   1   ☐ ☐

(i) $^-12$ $^-9$ $^-6$ $^-3$ ☐ ☐

(j) 32   16   8   4   ☐ ☐

(k) 1   2   4   7   ☐ ☐

(l) 1   2   5   10   ☐ ☐

(m) 20   19   17   14   ☐ ☐

(n) 1   4   9   16   ☐ ☐

(o) 1   1   2   3   5   8   ☐ ☐

3. Copy and complete these sequences:

(a) 3   6   9   ☐   15

(b) 12   10   8   ☐   4

(c) 4   8   12   ☐   20

(d) 25   20   15   ☐   5

(e) 7   14   ☐   28   35

(f) 3   7   ☐   15   19

(g) 1   10   ☐   28   37

(h) 5   ☐   11   14   17

(i) 50   ☐   42   38   34

(j) 2   ☐   8   16   32

(k) ☐   27   25   23   21

(l) ☐   17   20   23   26

(m) ☐   ⁻1   0   1   2

(n) ☐   2   ⁻1   ⁻4   ⁻7

(o) 20   40   ☐   80   100

(p) 25   ☐   75   100 125

(q) 200 ☐   100 50   0

(r) 2   4   ☐   8   10   ☐

(s) 13   11   ☐   7   5   ☐

(t) ☐   5   9   13   ☐   21

(u) 36   31   ☐   ☐   16   11

(v) 21   ☐   15   12   9   ☐

(w) ⁻6   ☐   2   6   ☐   14

(x) 1   2   4   ☐   11   16

(y) 20   19   17   ☐   10   5

Writing a sequence given a rule

You may be asked to form a sequence by following a rule given to you in words.

Examples:

(i) Start with 9
    Rule: Add 6
    Sequence: 9   15   21   27
                           (9 + 6)   (15 + 6)   (21 + 6)

(ii) Start with 3
    Rule: Multiply by 2 then add 1
    Sequence: 3   7   15   31
                       (3 × 2 + 1) (7 × 2 + 1) (15 × 2 + 1)

Exercise 11.2: Writing a sequence given a rule

Using the instruction given, write down the first four terms (including the starting number) of the following sequences:

1. Start with 3
    Rule: Add 2

2. Start with 2
    Rule: Multiply by 2

3. Start with 24
    Rule: Subtract 4

4. Start with 8
    Rule: Divide by 2

5. Start with 3
    Rule: Double

6. Start with 6
    Rule: Subtract 3

7. Start with $^-5$
    Rule: Add 3

8. Start with 7
    Rule: Multiply by 10

9. Start with 49
    Rule: Take away 11

10. Start with 25
    Rule: Add 25

11. Start with 1
    Rule: Add 5 then subtract 3

12. Start with 6
    Rule: Subtract 2 then add 6

13. Start with 3
    Rule: Multiply by 3 then subtract 4

14. Start with 1
    Rule: Multiply by 8 then divide by 4

15. Start with 2
    Rule: Multiply by 2 then add 2

16. Start with 2
    Rule: Add 2 then multiply by 2

17. Start with 5
    Rule: Multiply 2 then take away 1

18. Start with 5
    Rule: Take 1 away then multiply by 2

19. Start with 1
    Rule: Add 1 then treble

20. Start with 1
    Rule: Multiply by 2 then halve

End of chapter activity: Pascal's triangle

The diagram shows the first five lines of a pattern, or sequence, called Pascal's triangle. It was invented by a Frenchman named Pascal.

				1				
			1		1			
		1		2		1		
	1		3		3		1	
1		4		6		4		1

Study it carefully. Can you see how each line is formed from the line above it?

Copy the first five lines onto centimetre squared paper, then complete the next 5 or 6 lines.

Can you see any other patterns or sequences?

Did you know?

The **highest** temperature recorded in Great Britain was 38.5 °C (101.3 °F), at Faversham, Kent, on 10 August 2003

The **lowest** temperature recorded in Great Britain was ⁻27.2 °C (⁻17 °F) at Braemar, Scotland on 11 February 1895 and 10 January 1982, and at Altnaharra, Scotland, 30 December 1995

Chapter 12: Money

Sometimes you will come across different currencies used in other parts of the world. Don't worry! They are very like our money, but just with different names.

We have	100 pence = 1 pound	100p = £1
In most of Europe	100 cents = 1 euro	100c = €1
In the United States	100 cents = 1 dollar	100c = $1
In Gambia	100 bututs = 1 dalasi	

Can you think of any others?

· ·

Conversions

In the United Kingdom we know that there are 100 pence in 1 pound. This relationship between the number of pence and pounds is called a conversion. Let us look at some. Use the information above to help you.

To convert a sum of money **from pounds to pence** you need to **multiply by 100** (figures move 2 places to the left).

Example:	£2 = 200p
	£2.50 = 250p
	£1.75 = 175p

To convert from euros to cents, multiply by 100

Example:	€18 = 1800c
	€0.30 = 30c

To convert from US dollars to cents, multiply by 100

Example:	$4 = 400c
	$4.75 = 475c
	$0.05 = 5c

To convert sum of money **from pence to pounds** you need to **divide by 100** (figures move 2 places to the right).

Example: 200p = £2 (£2.00)
500p = £5 (£5.00)
325p = £3.25

To convert European cents to euros you also need to divide by 100

Example: 1600c = €16 (€16.00)
70c = €0.70

To convert US cents to dollars you need to divide by 100

Example: 600c = $6
825c = $8.25
1c = $0.01

Exercise 12.1: Conversion of money

1. Convert:

(a) £4 to pence

(b) €7 to cents

(c) $12 to cents

(d) £1.35 to pence

(e) €6.25 to cents

(f) $24.15 to cents

(g) £0.40 to pence

(h) €0.95 to cents

(i) $0.08 to cents

(j) $100 to cents

(k) €50 to cents

(l) £2000 to pence

2. Write:

(a) 900p in pounds

(b) 800c in euros

(c) 1700c in dollars

(d) 665p in pounds

(e) 148c in euros

(f) 950c in dollars

(g) 95p in pounds

(h) 5c in euros

(i) 10c in dollars

(j) 104p in pounds

(k) 140c in euros

(l) 410c in dollars

If you need to remind yourself of how to calculate money questions, look at Chapter 9 in *Junior Maths Book 1*.

Addition of money

Let us look at ways in which we can add amounts of money together. If the sums of money you have been asked to add together are in pence, you can set the question out like an ordinary addition.

Revision examples (Formal method)

Example: 47p + 78p

	H	T	U
		4	7
+		7	8
	1	2	5
		1	

Step 1: Put your sums of money in the correct columns.

Step 2: Add up the digits in the Units column
7 + 8 = 15 Remember to carry the 1 to the Tens column.

Step 3: Add up the digits in the Tens column, remembering to add in the carried number
4 + 7 + 1 = 12
= £1.25 (or 125p)

Remember if pounds and pence are used:

●   work in pounds; and

●   line up the decimal points under each other.

Examples: £3.76 + £19.42

(i)

	T	U			
		3	· 7	6	
+	1	9	· 4	2	
	2	3	· 1	8	= £23.18
	1	1			

(ii)   £27.45 + 89p + £6.74

	T	U		
	2	7·4		5
		0·8		9
+		6·7		4
	3	5·0		8
	1	2	1	

= £35.08

Exercise 12.2: Addition of money

You may be able to work out some of the answers without using a formal method. Be sure you can explain how you got your answer. Try these!

Calculate the following. Be careful to make sure that you write down your answers in the correct currency:

1. 37p + 42p

2. 75p + 58p

3. 49p + 67p

4. 24p + 36p + 7p

5. 93p + 5p + 29p

6. 8p + 38p + 47p

7. 89p + 8p + 93p

8. 83p + 64p + 76p

9. 95p + 79p + 68p

10. £1.50 + £2.00

11. £3.26 + £1.43

12. £4.76 + £3.49

13. £5.61 + £4.24

14. $2.00 + $6.50

15. $9.29 + $5.86

16. £27.38 + £3.80

17. €4.50 + €2.25

18. €8.49 + €27.75

19. £2.00 + £3.50 + £1.25

20. £1.63 + £2.48 + £5.82

21. £22.46 + £3.19 + £7.86

22. €9.34 + €11.69 + €2.23

23. £2.86 + 39p

24. 78p + £3.45

25. $21.63 + 67c

26. £4.27 + £0.84

27. €0.76 + €1.24

28. £4.38 + £2.16 + 94p

29. €8.62 + 39c + €26.25

30. 48c + 75c + $2.79

Subtraction of money

You can use the formal method of subtraction to subtract sums of money. When you subtract one sum of money from another, there are a few things you need to remember.

Revision examples (Formal method)

If pounds and pence are used:

● work in pounds; and

● line up the decimal points under each other.

Examples:

(i)   £19.55 − £17.25

	T	U		
	1	9 · 5	5
−	1	7 · 2	5
		2 · 3	0

Start on the right-hand side.

Step 1: 5 − 5 = 0

Step 2: 5 − 2 = 3

Step 3: 9 − 7 = 2

Step 4: 1 − 1 = 0

= £2.30

(ii)   £18.50 − £3.47

T	U			
1	8	.	⁴5̷	¹0
−		3	. 4	7
1	5	.	0	3

Step 1: You can't take 7 away from 0 so you need to take one from the next column on the left.

Step 2: Now you have 10 − 7 = 3

Step 3: 4 − 4 = 0

Step 4: 8 − 3 = 5

Step 5: 1 − 0 = 1

= £15.03

(iii)   £4.27 − 79p

T	U			
	³4̷	.	¹¹2̷	¹7
−			. 7	9
	3	.	4	8

= £3.48

(iv)   £5.00 − £1.37

T	U			
	⁴5̷	.	⁹0̷	¹0
−		1	. 3	7
	3	.	6	3

= £3.63

Whichever method you use, always remember to check your answer.

Exercise 12.3: Subtraction of money

You may be able to work out some of the answers without using a formal method. Be sure you can explain how you got your answer.

Calculate:

1. £3.43 – £1.82
2. £7.91 – £2.68
3. £4.15 – £2.57
4. £9.26 – £4.78
5. £8.34 – £1.86

6. €5.73 – €2.89
7. £6.32 – £4.71
8. $7.63 – $5.79
9. £4.00 – £1.37
10. £9.00 – £5.42

11. £3.25 – 68p
12. £7.14 – 59p
13. £5.00 – 37p
14. €6.50 – 78c
15. £27.70 – £4.95

16. £10.00 – £1.27
17. $50.00 – $27.30
18. £75.00 – £53.40
19. £50 – £4.36
20. €100 – €37.29

Multiplication of money

We have looked at addition and subtraction of money, so now let us look at how we multiply amounts of money. We can do this in much the same way as we multiplied numbers together in Chapter 6.

Examples (Formal method)

Method 1   87p x 6

	H	T	U
		8	7
×			6
		4	2
	4	8	0
	5	2	2
	1		

Set out your figures in the correct columns

Step 1: 6 x 7 = 42

Step 2: 6 x 80 = 480   (Note the 8 in the tens column is 80)

Step 3: 42 + 480 = 522

87p x 6 = 522p or £5.22

Method 2 87p x 6

	H	T	U	
		8	7	
x			6	
	5	2	2	
		4		

Step 1: 6 x 7 = 42 Put 2 in Units column and carry 4

Step 2: 6 x 8 = 48 plus carried 4 = 52

87p x 6 = £5.22

£3.48 x 4

	T	U		
		3 · 4	8	
x			4	
	1	3 · 9	2	
		1 3		

Step 1: 4 x 8 = 32 Write down 2 and carry 3

Step 2: 4 x 4 = 16 plus 3 = 19

Write down 9 and carry 1

Step 3: 4 x 3 = 12 plus 1 = 13

£3.48 x 4 = £13.92

Exercise 12.4: Multiplication of money

You may be able to work out some of the answers without using a formal method. Be sure you can explain how you got your answer.

Calculate:

1.   17p x 3

2.   38p x 4

3.   73p x 5

4.   42p x 6

5.   96p x 7

6.   64p x 8

7.   28p x 9

8.   57p x 10

9.   83p x 7

10. 49p x 8

11. £3.47 × 2

12. £1.34 × 3

13. $4.19 × 4

14. £7.63 × 5

15. €5.57 × 6

16. £3.08 × 7

17. £6.74 × 8

18. €8.52 × 9

19. £9.25 × 10

20. $2.73 × 4

21. £14.25 × 4

22. $17.40 × 3

23. €16.50 × 5

24. £21.75 × 2

25. £26.15 × 6

26. $23.80 × 8

27. £53.42 × 10

28. €43.09 × 10

29. £51.49 × 4

30. $62.38 × 5

Division of money

Informal method of division

Let us start by using the informal method of division. This is where we think of division as repeated subtraction. It may help to look at *Junior Maths Book 1* pages 85–6 and here in Chapter 7.

Examples:

(i)   72p ÷ 4

	7	2
−	4	0
	3	2
−	3	2
	0	0

You know that (**10** lots of 4) is 40
72 − 40 = 32

(**8** lots of 4)
When you reach 00 you have come to the end of your calculation.

To get your answer look at how many lots of 4 you have subtracted (**10** + **8** = **18** lots of 4)

So we have calculated that 72p ÷ 4 = 18p

(ii) 84p ÷ 3

	8	4
−	3	0
	5	4
−	3	0
	2	4
−	2	4
	0	0

(**10** lots of 3)

(**10** lots of 3)

(**8** lots of 3)
(10 + 10 + 8 = 28)
84p ÷ 3 = 28p

or

	8	4
−	6	0
	2	4
−	2	4
	0	0

(**20** lots of 3)

(**8** lots of 3)
(20 + 8 = 28)
84p ÷ 3 = 28p

(iii) If the number of pounds is less than the number you are dividing by **work in pence** because your answer will be in pence.

£3.90 ÷ 5
(£3.90 = 390p)

	3	9	0
−	3	5	0
		4	0
		4	0
		0	0

(**70** lots of 5)

(**8** lots of 5)
(70 + 8 = 78)

£3.90 ÷ 5 = 78p

(iv) If the number of pounds is equal to, or more than, the number you are dividing by split the sum into 2 parts.

Divide the pounds and then divide what remains in pence.

£13.48 ÷ 4

Step 1: First look the number of pounds and divide by 4

£13 ÷ 4 = **£3** with £1 (or 100p) remaining

Step 2: Now add the remaining £1 (or 100p) to the 48p from the original amount

100p + 48p = 148p and divide this by 4

	1	4	8
−	1	2	0
		2	8
−		2	8
		0	0

(**30** lots of 4)

(**7** lots of 4)

(30 + 7 = 37)

£1.48 ÷ 4 = **37p**

Finally add the **£3** from **Step 1** to the **37p** from **Step 2** to give **£3.37**

We can now give the answer £13.48 ÷ 4 = £3.37

Exercise 12.5: Division of money (1)

Calculate the following:

1. 51p ÷ 3
2. 68p ÷ 4
3. 85p ÷ 5
4. 96c ÷ 4
5. 91p ÷ 7

6. 76p ÷ 2
7. 72p ÷ 3
8. 90c ÷ 6
9. 54p ÷ 2
10. 81c ÷ 3

11. £1.26 ÷ 2
12. £2.16 ÷ 3
13. €3.48 ÷ 4
14. £3.65 ÷ 5
15. $2.70 ÷ 6

16. £2.76 ÷ 4
17. $1.53 ÷ 9
18. £2.72 ÷ 8
19. €4.32 ÷ 6
20. £5.25 ÷ 7

21. £6.15 ÷ 5
22. £8.26 ÷ 7
23. $4.35 ÷ 3
24. £3.36 ÷ 2
25. €8.76 ÷ 6

26. £10.32 ÷ 4
27. $18.27 ÷ 7
28. £16.75 ÷ 5
29. £14.20 ÷ 10
30. €18.56 ÷ 8

Formal method of division

Now let us look at dividing money using the formal method of division. You can remind yourself of this method by looking back at *Junior Maths Book 1* page 90.

This method will usually save you time.

Examples:

(i)   72p ÷ 4

	1	
4	7	³2

Step 1: There is 1 x 4 in 7 with 3 remainder

Put 1 in the answer and carry 3

	1	8
4	7	³2

Step 2: There are 8 x 4 in 32

Put 8 in the answer

72p ÷ 4 = 18p

(ii)   72p ÷ 3

	2	
3	7	¹2

Step 1: There are 2 x 3 in 7 with 1 remainder

Put 2 in the answer and carry 1

	2	4
3	7	¹2

Step 2: There are 4 x 3 in 12

72p ÷ 3 = 24p

(iii) £3.90 ÷ 5   [change into pence]

5	3	9	0

Step 1: There are 0 x 5 in 3

So look at 39

		7	
5	3	9	⁴0

Step 2: There are 7 x 5 in 39 with 4 remainder

Put 7 in the answer and carry 4

		7	8
5	3	9	⁴0

Step 3: There are 8 x 5 in 40

Put 8 in the answer

£3.90 ÷ 5 = 78p

(iv) £53.48 ÷ 4

Step 1: There is 1 x 4 in 5 with 1 remainder

Put 1 in the answer and carry 1

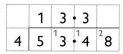

Step 2: There are 3 x 4 in 13 with 1 remainder

Put 3 in the answer and carry 1

	1	3 · 3			
4	5	¹3 · ¹4	²8

Step 3: There are 3 x 4 in 14 with 2 remainder

Put 3 in the answer and carry 2

	1	3 · 3	7		
4	5	¹3 · ¹4	²8

Step 4: There are 7 x 4 in 28

Put 7 in the answer

£53.48 ÷ 4 = £13.37

Note: in each example above the division calculation has been written out again at each step to help show what is happening. When you do informal calculations you do not have to. Instead yours should look like the examples on the next page.

Examples:

(i)   84p ÷ 4

	2	1
4	8	4

84p ÷ 4 = 21p

(ii)   £7.25 ÷ 5

	1	4	5
5	7	²2	²5

£7.25 ÷ 5 = £1.45

Exercise 12.6: Division of money (2)

Use the formal method to calculate the following. Be careful to give your answer in the correct currency:

1.   58p ÷ 2

2.   76p ÷ 4

3.   84c ÷ 3

4.   65p ÷ 5

5.   60c ÷ 6

6.   96p ÷ 8

7.   75c ÷ 3

8.   90p ÷ 5

9.   84p ÷ 7

10. 94c ÷ 2

11. £1.78 ÷ 2

12. £1.71 ÷ 3

13. £2.64 ÷ 4

14. $4.35 ÷ 5

15. £3.54 ÷ 6

16. €5.25 ÷ 7

17. £6.80 ÷ 8

18. £4.05 ÷ 9

19. $3.42 ÷ 6

20. £3.44 ÷ 4

21. £3.76 ÷ 2

22. £5.16 ÷ 4

23. €7.60 ÷ 5

24. £5.22 ÷ 3

25. $9.54 ÷ 6

26. £5.58 ÷ 2

27. €7.29 ÷ 3

28. £10.52 ÷ 4

29. $12.35 ÷ 5

30. £20.34 ÷ 6

31. £21.80 ÷ 4

32. €23.40 ÷ 5

33. £15.26 ÷ 7

34. £28.00 ÷ 8

35. $19.08 ÷ 9

Exercise 12.7: One-step problems

Use any method you wish, but you should show some working to explain how you arrived at your answer.

Remember, if you only give an answer and it is wrong, you won't be given any marks. However, if you show your workings and your teacher can see that you do actually know the method but have just made a silly mistake, you might possibly get some marks!

1. Stamps cost either 34 pence or 48 pence. Max buys one of each. How much does Max pay for the 2 stamps?

2. Jack buys a cherry tart for 39 pence and a cream horn for 75 pence. How much does Jack pay altogether?

3. Sam buys *Robot* magazine for £2.85 and the *Courier* newspaper for 70 pence.
   How much does Sam spend in total?

4. Wayne goes to watch a football match. His train fare is £1.86, his entrance fee costs £1.50 and he spends 99 pence on a meat pie. What does it cost Wayne altogether to watch the match?

5. Belle spends $17.40 on bubble bath and $5.75 on eye shadow. What do these items cost Belle altogether?

6. A bar of chocolate costs 54 pence and a packet of crisps costs 27 pence.
   How much cheaper are the crisps than the chocolate?

7. Jenny buys a pot of jam for £1.27 and pays for it with a £2 coin.
   How much change should she receive?

8. A teapot costs £4.40 and the matching milk jug costs £2.80 less.
   What is the cost of the jug?

9. A doll is priced at €57.50. So far Marie has saved €45.75 towards the price of the doll.
   How much more must Marie save to be able to buy the doll?

10. The usual price of a DVD player is £102.50 but in the sale the price is reduced by £52.51.
    What is the sale price of the DVD player?

11. Pencils cost 17 pence each.
    What is the cost of 5 pencils?

12. The price of a large marker pen is 89 pence.
    How much does Mr. Winkle pay for a box of 6 pens?

13. Cinema tickets cost either £3.95 or £4.40 each.
    A group of 8 go to the cinema and buy the more expensive tickets.
    How much does it cost for this group to go to the cinema?

14. It costs £375 per month to hire a car.
    What does Roy pay to hire the car for 3 months?

15. A journey on *Eurostar* costs €87.45
    How much does it cost 4 people to make this journey?

16. 3 packets of toffees cost £1.35
    What is the cost of 1 packet of toffees?

17. 5 apple pies cost $6.25
    What does 1 apple pie cost?

18. 8 bottles of olive oil cost £20.56
    What does 1 bottle cost?

19. A pair of shoes normally costs £37.60. In the sale, prices are reduced by a quarter.
    By how much is the price of the shoes reduced in the sale?

20. 6 rose bushes cost £39
    What is the cost of 1 rose bush?

Exercise 12.8: Two-step problems

1. Bread rolls cost 18 pence each or on offer at '6 for 84p'.
   Which is the cheaper way to buy 6 rolls and how much is saved?

2. A table costs £180 and the chairs are priced at £37.50 each.
   What is the total cost of a table and 6 chairs?

3. The train fare to Blackstone is £3.90 for adults, and children travel at half the adult fare. How much does it cost Mrs Muggins and her 3 children to go by train to Blackstone?

4. Mr Felton takes his 3 children to a model railway exhibition.
   Mr Felton pays £7.25 for all of them to enter. He pays £3.50 for himself.
   How much is a child's entrance fee?

5. Jason buys a model boat which costs £60. He pays £40 and promises the shopkeeper that he will pay the rest of the money over the next 4 weeks.
   How much will he pay weekly if he pays the same amount each time?

6. A group of 8 friends share 3 pizzas equally.
   What should each friend pay if a pizza costs £4.40?

7. Rosemary is on holiday in Portugal and sends 12 postcards to friends at home. The cost of sending a postcard is 61 cents.
How much change should she receive from €10?

8. Sheena has a $10 note in her purse. She buys 8 waffles for 95 cents each and a jar of maple syrup for $2.70
Does Sheena have enough money to pay for all these items?
What do you suggest Sheena does so that she can buy as much as possible?

9.

Benito's Ice Cream Parlour	
Price list	
Ice cream (any flavour)	80p
Flaky white	99p
Chocky mint	£1.15
Strawberry sundae	£1.40

The Benson family order:
2 vanilla ice creams
2 mango ice creams
1 chocky mint
3 strawberry sundaes

(a) How much does the Benson family's bill add up to?

(b) How much change should there be from £20?

10.

Rose Blossom Tea Rooms	
Cream teas ~ Everything home-made	
Pot of tea	£1.15 per person
Scones	35 pence each
Strawberry jam	45 pence
Clotted cream	90 pence
Chocolate cake	95 pence per slice

Elsie and Doris order:
a pot of tea for 2
4 scones
2 jams
1 cream
2 cakes

Elsie and Doris share the bill between them. How much does each pay?

End of chapter activity: Money round the world

At the beginning of the chapter you were told that many countries have their unit of money based on 100.

> There are 100 pence in the pound (£)
> 100 cents in the euro (€)
> 100 cents in the dollar ($)

Your task is to find another 20 countries who also have their unit of money based on 100. (One was mentioned at the beginning of the chapter). To make it a little harder, you are not allowed to use the dollar again: no Canadian dollar, Australian dollar etc.

At the end see how many different countries your class has found. Good luck!

Did you know?

The most expensive area to live in the United Kingdom is Kensington Palace Gardens in London. Among your neighbours would be the French and Russian ambassadors.

The most expensive shopping area in the United Kingdom is London's Oxford Street which is also the longest shopping street in Europe. Perhaps the most famous store is Selfridges which has been on its site for more than 100 years. Oxford Street is also famous for its Christmas street decorations which attract millions of visitors every year.

Chapter 13: Fractions

So far, all the **fractions** you have seen have been less than 1

A fraction is a piece of a whole, so you might think that all fractions must be less than 1, but this isn't true.

Let's look at some groups of fractions. What happens if they add up to more than 1?

Examples:

(i)   You know that two halves make one whole ($\frac{2}{2}$ = 1).

What happens if we have more than two halves?

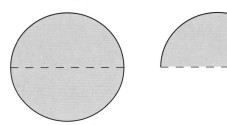

A disc is made up of two halves.

Here we have three halves. Together they make up one whole disc with one half left over.

$$\frac{1}{2} + \frac{1}{2} + \frac{1}{2} = \frac{3}{2} = 1\frac{1}{2}$$

(ii)   You know that four quarters make one whole ($\frac{4}{4}$ = 1).

What happens if we have more than four quarters?

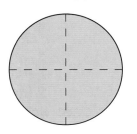 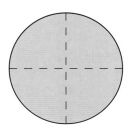 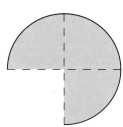

This time the disc is made up of four quarters.

Here we have eleven quarters. Together they make up two whole discs with three quarters left over.

$$\frac{1}{4} + \frac{1}{4} + \frac{1}{4} + \frac{1}{4} + \frac{1}{4} + \frac{1}{4} + \frac{1}{4} + \frac{1}{4} + \frac{1}{4} + \frac{1}{4} + \frac{1}{4} = \frac{11}{4} = 2\frac{3}{4}$$

Different kinds of fractions have different names:

- A fraction less than 1 is a **proper fraction**.

  $\frac{1}{2}$ and $\frac{1}{4}$ are proper fractions. $\frac{1}{2} < 1$ $\frac{1}{4} < 1$

- A fraction greater than 1 is an **improper fraction**.

  $\frac{3}{2}$ and $\frac{11}{4}$ are improper fractions. $\frac{3}{2} > 1$ $\frac{11}{4} > 1$

- A whole number and fraction together make a **mixed number**.

  $1\frac{1}{2}$ and $2\frac{3}{4}$ are mixed numbers.

Writing improper fractions as whole numbers or mixed numbers

We can write an improper fraction as a whole number or mixed number using **division**.

Remember:

- The top of a fraction shows $\longrightarrow$ number of equal parts there are

  The bottom of a fraction shows $\longrightarrow$ number of equal parts the unit has been divided into

- The bottom of a fraction gives it its name

Ally 27/1/19

Examples:

(i) Write $\frac{12}{3}$ as a whole number.

There are 3 thirds in a whole number, we know this from the 3 in the bottom part of this fraction.

There are 12 thirds altogether. How many whole numbers is this?

$12 \div 3 = 4$

So, 12 is exactly 4 lots of 3

So $\frac{12}{3} = 4$

(ii) Write $\frac{13}{5}$ as a mixed number.

There are 5 fifths in a whole number.

There are 13 fifths altogether.

$13 \div 5 = 2$ remainder 3

So, 13 is 2 lots of 5 with 3 fifths left over.

$\frac{13}{5} = 2\frac{3}{5}$

(iii) Write $\frac{22}{8}$ as a mixed number.

There are 8 eighths in a whole number.

There are 22 eighths altogether.

$22 \div 8 = 2$ remainder 6

So, 22 is 2 lots of 8 with 6 eighths left over.

$\frac{22}{8} = 2\frac{6}{8} = 2\frac{3}{4}$

Note: In Example (iii), did you notice that $2\frac{6}{8}$ was not in its lowest terms? Both top and bottom of the fraction could be divided by 2, to give $2\frac{3}{4}$

27.1.19 ALL

Exercise 13.1: Writing improper fractions as whole numbers or mixed numbers

Find ✓

1. Write the following as whole numbers:

(a) $\frac{3}{3}$

(b) $\frac{4}{4}$

(c) $\frac{10}{2}$

(d) $\frac{15}{5}$

(e) $\frac{14}{7}$

(f) $\frac{24}{8}$

(g) $\frac{30}{5}$

(h) $\frac{27}{9}$

(i) $\frac{40}{10}$

(j) $\frac{36}{12}$

2. Write the following as mixed numbers:

(a) $\frac{7}{6}$

(b) $\frac{10}{7}$

(c) $\frac{11}{8}$

(d) $\frac{13}{10}$

(e) $\frac{9}{5}$

(f) $\frac{7}{3}$

(g) $\frac{13}{5}$

(h) $\frac{11}{4}$

(i) $\frac{17}{7}$

(j) $\frac{20}{9}$

(k) $\frac{19}{6}$

(l) $\frac{33}{10}$

(m) $\frac{21}{8}$

(n) $\frac{24}{5}$

(o) $\frac{13}{2}$

(p) $\frac{23}{3}$

(q) $\frac{27}{4}$

(r) $\frac{41}{6}$

(s) $\frac{35}{8}$

(t) $\frac{49}{10}$

3. Write the following as mixed numbers, with the fractions in their lowest terms:

(a) $\frac{12}{8}$

(b) $\frac{12}{9}$

(c) $\frac{10}{4}$

(d) $\frac{16}{6}$

(e) $\frac{26}{10}$

(f) $\frac{15}{12}$

(g) $\frac{24}{20}$

(h) $\frac{18}{15}$

(i) $\frac{18}{12}$

(j) $\frac{35}{20}$

(k) $\frac{18}{14}$

(l) $\frac{22}{16}$

(m) $\frac{45}{30}$

(n) $\frac{35}{25}$

(o) $\frac{50}{40}$

Fractions and division

You already know how to divide whole numbers.

> **Example:** $17 \div 3 = 5$ remainder 2

This is the same as $\frac{17}{3} = 5\frac{2}{3}$

So if you get a remainder when you do a division, you can write that remainder as a fraction:

> **Example:** $17 \div 3 = 5\frac{2}{3}$

Exercise 13.2: Fractions and division

Calculate the following, giving the answers as mixed numbers:

1. $12 \div 7$
2. $14 \div 5$
3. $17 \div 8$
4. $35 \div 6$
5. $19 \div 5$

6. $29 \div 9$
7. $19 \div 4$
8. $25 \div 6$
9. $23 \div 7$
10. $37 \div 10$

Writing mixed numbers as improper fractions

We can write a mixed number as an improper fraction using **multiplication**.

First look at the bottom number in the fraction part of the mixed number. This doesn't change, so you already know the name of the improper fraction.

Examples:

(i) Write $1\frac{2}{3}$ as an improper fraction.

There are 3 thirds in a whole number. So, the 1 is the same as $\frac{3}{3}$

Add on the 2 thirds to the 3 thirds from the whole number so, there are $3 + 2 = 5$ thirds altogether

$$1\frac{2}{3} = \frac{5}{3}$$

(ii) Write $3\frac{4}{5}$ as an improper fraction.

There are 5 fifths in a whole number: there are $3 \times 5 = 15$ fifths in 3

Add on the 4 fifths: there are $15 + 4$ fifths altogether.

$$3\frac{4}{5} = \frac{19}{5}$$

Exercise 13.3: Writing mixed numbers as improper fractions

Write the following as improper fractions:

1. $1\frac{1}{2}$

2. $1\frac{3}{4}$

3. $1\frac{7}{10}$

4. $1\frac{5}{6}$

5. $2\frac{2}{3}$

6. $2\frac{3}{5}$

7. $2\frac{7}{12}$

8. $2\frac{11}{15}$

9. $3\frac{4}{5}$

10. $3\frac{7}{9}$

11. $3\frac{9}{10}$

12. $4\frac{2}{3}$

13. $4\frac{4}{7}$

14. $4\frac{3}{10}$

15. $4\frac{8}{11}$

16. $5\frac{2}{3}$

17. $5\frac{6}{7}$

18. $5\frac{8}{9}$

19. $6\frac{1}{8}$

20. $7\frac{1}{2}$

21. $4\frac{1}{6}$

22. $8\frac{1}{3}$

23. $1\frac{19}{20}$

24. $2\frac{13}{15}$

25. $2\frac{7}{25}$

26. $3\frac{5}{12}$

27. $4\frac{8}{9}$

28. $6\frac{3}{4}$

29. $7\frac{1}{3}$

30. $10\frac{3}{5}$

Ordering fractions (1)

It is easy to see that:

- $\frac{3}{8}$ is greater than $\frac{1}{8}$ $\frac{3}{8} > \frac{1}{8}$

- $\frac{3}{8}$ is less than $\frac{7}{8}$ $\frac{3}{8} < \frac{7}{8}$

The fractions have the same name (eighths) and 3 is greater than 1 but less than 7

If we want to compare the size of two fractions with different names, such as $\frac{2}{3}$ and $\frac{5}{9}$, we must write them as **equivalent fractions** first.

Remember: Equivalent fractions are **equal**. We find them by multiplying or dividing both the top and bottom of the fraction by the same number.

Examples:

(i)   Which fraction is larger, $\frac{2}{3}$ or $\frac{5}{9}$?

    $\frac{2}{3}$ can be changed into $\frac{6}{9}$ by multiplying top and bottom by 3

    $\frac{6}{9}$ is larger than $\frac{5}{9}$ so,

    $\frac{2}{3}$ is larger than $\frac{5}{9}$

(ii)   Which fraction is larger, $\frac{7}{10}$ or $\frac{4}{5}$?

    $\frac{4}{5}$ can be changed into $\frac{8}{10}$ by multiplying top and bottom by 2

    $\frac{8}{10}$ is larger than $\frac{7}{10}$ so,

    $\frac{4}{5}$ is larger than $\frac{7}{10}$

Exercise 13.4 Ordering fractions (1)

1. Write these fractions in order of size, starting with the **larger**:

(a) $\frac{1}{2}$ $\frac{5}{8}$ (f) $\frac{5}{9}$ $\frac{11}{18}$

(b) $\frac{7}{12}$ $\frac{1}{2}$ (g) $\frac{9}{10}$ $\frac{17}{20}$

(c) $\frac{5}{6}$ $\frac{2}{3}$ (h) $\frac{3}{4}$ $\frac{13}{20}$

(d) $\frac{3}{4}$ $\frac{7}{12}$ (i) $\frac{1}{3}$ $\frac{7}{15}$

(e) $\frac{1}{4}$ $\frac{3}{8}$ (j) $\frac{13}{16}$ $\frac{3}{4}$

2. Write these fractions in order of size, starting with the **smaller**:

(a) $\frac{5}{6}$ $\frac{11}{12}$ (f) $\frac{5}{8}$ $\frac{11}{16}$

(b) $\frac{1}{3}$ $\frac{4}{9}$ (g) $\frac{3}{15}$ $\frac{2}{3}$

(c) $\frac{9}{10}$ $\frac{4}{5}$ (h) $\frac{1}{4}$ $\frac{7}{20}$

(d) $\frac{5}{6}$ $\frac{13}{18}$ (i) $\frac{1}{3}$ $\frac{7}{24}$

(e) $\frac{6}{7}$ $\frac{11}{14}$ (j) $\frac{5}{7}$ $\frac{17}{21}$

Lowest common multiple

Have another look at the questions in Exercise 13.4. For each pair of fractions, you could multiply one bottom number by a number to make the second bottom number.

When you can't do this, you have to multiply both the bottom numbers to find a new common name.

The new common name will be a **multiple** of both the bottom numbers from the original fractions.

For example, if we wanted to compare the fractions $\frac{5}{6}$ and $\frac{7}{8}$ we would need to find a number that is a multiple of both 6 and 8

Multiples of 6:	6	12	18	**24**	30	36	42	**48**
Multiples of 8:	8	16	**24**	32	40	**48**	56	64

Look for the numbers that appear in both the multiples of 6 row and the multiples of 8 row.

You can see two **common multiples** of 6 and 8: 24 and 48

We call 24 the **lowest common multiple (LCM)** of 6 and 8

24 will be easier to work with than 48: as a rule it is easier to work with smaller, rather than larger, numbers.

The quickest way to find the LCM of two or more numbers is to go through the multiples of the largest number until you find the first one that is also in the other times table(s).

Examples:

(i)   What is the LCM of 9 and 12?

Multiples of 12:   12   24   36

36 is the first multiple of 12 that is also in the 9 times table.

36 is the LCM of 9 and 12

(ii)   What is the LCM of 2, 4 and 5?

Multiples of 5:   5   10   15   20

20 is the first multiple of 5 that is also in the 2 and 4 times tables (10 is in the 2 times table but not in the 4 times table.)

20 is the LCM of 2, 4 and 5

Sometimes the LCM is one of the numbers (this is what happened in Exercise 13.4)

- 12 is the LCM of 6 and 12
- 15 is the LCM of 3, 5 and 15

Exercise 13.5: Lowest common multiple

Write down the lowest common multiple of the following numbers:

1. 2 and 3
2. 3 and 4
3. 4 and 6
4. 6 and 9

5. 6 and 10
6. 6 and 12
7. 8 and 10
8. 8 and 12

9. 2, 3 and 4
10. 2, 3 and 6
11. 2, 3 and 8
12. 2, 5 and 6

13. 3, 4 and 6
14. 3, 4 and 8
15. 3, 4 and 9

· ·

Ordering fractions (2)

When you use the lowest common multiple to compare fractions, you must take care to multiply the tops of the fractions by the correct number.

Examples:

(i) Which fraction is larger, $\frac{5}{6}$ or $\frac{7}{8}$?

Step 1: Find the LCM of 6 and 8: this is 24

Step 2: Write both fractions as 24ths:

$\frac{5}{6} = \frac{20}{24}$

6 is multiplied by 4 to make 24 (the 4th multiple of 6), so we must multiply the top by 4 as well.

$\frac{7}{8} = \frac{21}{24}$

8 is multiplied by 3 to make 24 (the 3rd multiple of 8), so we must multiply the top by 3 as well.

Step 3: Compare the fractions:

$\frac{21}{24} > \frac{20}{24}$ so $\frac{7}{8} > \frac{5}{6}$

So $\frac{7}{8}$ is larger.

(ii) Write $\frac{2}{3}, \frac{3}{4}$ and $\frac{5}{9}$ in order, starting with the **smallest**.

Step 1: Find the LCM of 3, 4 and 9: 36

Step 2: Write all three fractions as 36ths:

$\frac{2}{3} = \frac{24}{36}$ 3 is multiplied by 12 to make 36 (the 12th multiple of 3), so we must multiply the top by 12 as well.

$\frac{3}{4} = \frac{27}{36}$ 4 is multiplied by 9 to make 36 (the 9th multiple of 4), so we must multiply the top by 9 as well.

$\frac{5}{9} = \frac{20}{36}$ 9 is multiplied by 4 to make 36 (the 4th multiple of 9), so we must multiply the top by 4 as well.

Step 3: Order the fractions.

$$\frac{20}{36} < \frac{24}{36} < \frac{27}{36} \text{ so } \frac{5}{9} < \frac{2}{3} < \frac{3}{4}$$

Starting with the smallest: $\frac{5}{9}, \frac{2}{3}, \frac{3}{4}$

Exercise 13.6: Ordering fractions (2)

1. Which of each pair of fractions is the **larger**?

(a) $\frac{1}{2}$ $\frac{2}{3}$ (f) $\frac{7}{12}$ $\frac{3}{4}$

(b) $\frac{2}{5}$ $\frac{1}{3}$ (g) $\frac{3}{5}$ $\frac{2}{3}$

(c) $\frac{3}{4}$ $\frac{2}{3}$ (h) $\frac{7}{12}$ $\frac{5}{9}$

(d) $\frac{9}{10}$ $\frac{4}{5}$ (i) $\frac{3}{5}$ $\frac{7}{10}$

(e) $\frac{1}{2}$ $\frac{3}{7}$ (j) $\frac{5}{6}$ $\frac{9}{10}$

2. Write these fractions in order of size, starting with the **largest**:

(a) $\frac{1}{2}$ $\frac{3}{4}$ $\frac{5}{8}$

(b) $\frac{3}{4}$ $\frac{4}{5}$ $\frac{7}{10}$

(c) $\frac{7}{8}$ $\frac{3}{4}$ $\frac{11}{12}$

(d) $\frac{3}{4}$ $\frac{4}{5}$ $\frac{7}{8}$

(e) $\frac{2}{9}$ $\frac{1}{6}$ $\frac{1}{3}$

3. Which of each pair of fractions is the **smaller?**

(a) $\frac{1}{2}$ $\frac{4}{9}$ (f) $\frac{13}{20}$ $\frac{5}{8}$

(b) $\frac{1}{3}$ $\frac{3}{8}$ (g) $\frac{1}{6}$ $\frac{2}{9}$

(c) $\frac{7}{10}$ $\frac{2}{3}$ (h) $\frac{2}{3}$ $\frac{11}{15}$

(d) $\frac{3}{4}$ $\frac{5}{6}$ (i) $\frac{7}{8}$ $\frac{4}{5}$

(e) $\frac{2}{3}$ $\frac{4}{5}$ (j) $\frac{3}{4}$ $\frac{17}{20}$

4. Write these fractions in order of size, starting with the **smallest**:

(a) $\frac{3}{4}$ $\frac{5}{6}$ $\frac{2}{3}$

(b) $\frac{2}{3}$ $\frac{8}{15}$ $\frac{4}{5}$

(c) $\frac{1}{2}$ $\frac{2}{3}$ $\frac{4}{9}$

(d) $\frac{2}{3}$ $\frac{7}{12}$ $\frac{3}{4}$

(e) $\frac{3}{5}$ $\frac{2}{3}$ $\frac{1}{2}$

Exercise 13.7: Summary exercise

1. Write the following improper fractions as mixed numbers:

   (a) $\frac{9}{2}$

   (b) $\frac{14}{5}$

   (c) $\frac{27}{4}$

   (d) $\frac{19}{8}$

   (e) $\frac{21}{6}$

2. Calculate the following, giving your answers as mixed numbers:

   (a) $11 \div 2$

   (b) $23 \div 5$

   (c) $30 \div 7$

   (d) $22 \div 7$

   (e) $30 \div 4$

3. Write the following mixed numbers as improper fractions:

   (a) $1\frac{2}{3}$

   (b) $3\frac{1}{2}$

   (c) $5\frac{3}{4}$

   (d) $2\frac{3}{5}$

   (e) $4\frac{5}{8}$

4. What is the lowest common multiple of these numbers?

   (a) 3   4

   (b) 6   8

   (c) 6   9

   (d) 6   12

   (e) 2   3   4

   (f) 2   3   5

   (g) 3   4   8

   (h) 3   5   15

5. Write these fractions in order of size, starting with the **largest**:

   (a) $\frac{5}{8}$ $\frac{11}{16}$

   (b) $\frac{5}{7}$ $\frac{2}{3}$

   (c) $\frac{4}{5}$ $\frac{3}{4}$

   (d) $\frac{1}{2}$ $\frac{8}{15}$ $\frac{3}{5}$

   (e) $\frac{2}{3}$ $\frac{3}{4}$ $\frac{7}{12}$

6. Write these fractions in order of size, starting with the **smallest**:

   (a) $\frac{2}{3}$ $\frac{5}{9}$

   (b) $\frac{4}{5}$ $\frac{3}{4}$

   (c) $\frac{5}{6}$ $\frac{7}{8}$

   (d) $\frac{5}{6}$ $\frac{2}{3}$ $\frac{8}{9}$

   (e) $\frac{3}{10}$ $\frac{2}{5}$ $\frac{1}{3}$

End of chapter activity: Four and twenty

Try to make all the numbers from 0 to 20 using only the number 4

You can use any mathematical signs.

Example: The number 1 could be written as $4 \div 4$ or as a fraction $\frac{4}{4}$

How can you make 2?

Share your calculations with your classmates. Did you make any of the numbers in different ways?

Did you know?

The chance of matching six numbers in a lottery draw such as the one played in Britain, and winning the jackpot is **13 983 816 to 1**

This is nearly **14 million to 1**, so not very likely!

The chance of matching three numbers and winning £10 is about **57 to 1**

This means that if you buy one ticket every Saturday, you are likely to win once a year.

The tickets cost £1 each so 1 ticket a week for a year will cost you about £52

Do you think this is a good deal?

Chapter 14: Introduction to decimals

We have already come across **decimals** when we write sums of money (Chapter 12). The **decimal point** separates the pounds from the pence.

	£7	•	25
	whole pounds	decimal point	pence (bits of a pound)

In the same way the decimal point separates the **integers** (whole numbers) from the **decimal fractions** (the bits of a whole number).

	7	•	25
	whole numbers	decimal point	decimal fractions

We read this as **seven point two five**. Notice that each figure to the **right** of the decimal point is read individually.

The figures to the right of the decimal point are in **decimal places**.

- The **first** figure to the right of the point is the **first place of decimals**.

- The **second** figure to the right of the point is the **second place of decimals**.

- The third figure to the right of the point is the **third place of decimals**. And so on.

Place value and decimals

In Chapter 1 we learnt about place value, but then we looked only at **integers** (whole numbers). Now we can extend what we already know to include **decimals**.

Hundreds	Tens	Units	•	tenths	hundredths	thousandths
100	10	1	•	$\frac{1}{10}$	$\frac{1}{100}$	$\frac{1}{1000}$
H	T	U	•	t	h	th

Each column is 10 times smaller than its left-hand neighbour.

$$100 \div 10 = 10 \quad 10 \div 10 = 1 \quad \bullet \quad 1 \div 10 = \frac{1}{10} \quad \frac{1}{10} \div 10 = \frac{1}{100} \quad \frac{1}{100} \div 10 = \frac{1}{1000}$$

Remember: $\frac{1}{10}$ means $1 \div 10$

0.2, 0.5 and 0.8 are numbers between 0 and 1

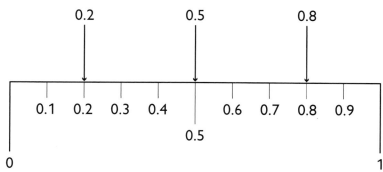

1.3, 2.5 and 3.7 are numbers between 0 and 5

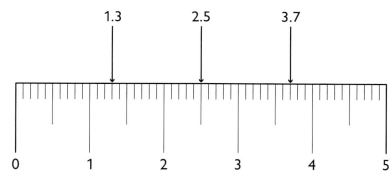

4.23, 4.65 and 4.87 are numbers between 4 and 5

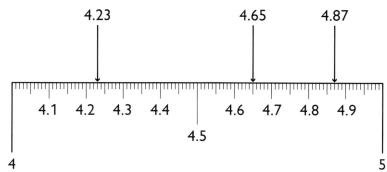

As we learnt in Chapter 1, the values of the digits in an integer (whole number) depend on their **place values**.

Examples: What is the real value of the underlined digit?

(i)

H	T	U
5	<u>8</u>	6

The 8 is in the **Tens** column so its value is 80

(ii)

H	T	U
<u>1</u>	5	9

The 1 is in the **Hundreds** column so its value is 100

(iii)

H	T	U
8	3	<u>7</u>

The 7 is in the **Units** column so its value is 7

The same is true of digits on the right of the decimal point (decimal fractions). Don't forget the decimal point, remember to write it down in the correct place.

Examples: What is the real value of the underlined digit?

(i)

U	t	h
0	<u>9</u>	3

The 9 is in the **tenths** column so its value is $\frac{9}{10}$

(ii)

U	t	h
0	4	<u>7</u>

The 7 is in the **hundredths** column so its value is $\frac{7}{100}$

(iii)

U	t	h	th
0	9	5	<u>1</u>

The 1 is in the **thousandths** column so its value is $\frac{1}{1000}$

Exercise 14.1: Place value and decimals

Write down the real value of the underlined digits. Set out the values carefully in the correct columns as shown in the examples above. If you do this carefully it will help you to work out the answer.

1.

U	t	h
0	3	

2.

U	t	h
0	5	7

3.

U	t	h	th
0	1	8	7

4. 0.932

5. 0.941

6. 0.708

7. 0.999

8. 0.999

9. 0.999

10. 0.73

11. 7.39

12. 9.177

13. 4.315

14. 26.137

15. 26.137

16. 26.137

17. 26.137

18. 26.137

19. 296.43

20. 296.43

21. 89.3

22. 89.3

23. 4200.147

24. 4200.147

25. 632.2

Ordering decimals

When we compare decimals, we must compare the figures in the same place value columns.

Examples:

(i) Write down the larger number of 0.6 and 0.39

U	t	h
0	6	

and

U	t	h
0	3	9

39 may look larger than 6 but they are not whole numbers.

Look at just the **tenths** digits. 0.**6** and 0.**3**9

0.6 is larger because 6 tenths ($\frac{6}{10}$) is larger than 3 tenths ($\frac{3}{10}$)

(ii) Write down the smaller number of 0.09 and 0.2

U	t	h
0	0	9

and

U	t	h
0	2	

2 may look smaller than 9 but they are not whole numbers.

Look at just the **tenths** digits. 0.**0**9 and 0.**2**

0.09 is smaller because 0 tenths (0) is smaller than 2 tenths ($\frac{2}{10}$)

Exercise 14.2: Ordering decimals (1)

You may find it helpful to set the numbers out in their correct columns as shown in Q.1 (a) and (b) below:

1. Write down the larger number:

(a)

U	t	h
0	8	

U	t	h
0	3	

(b)

U	t	h
0	3	7

U	t	h
0	6	2

(c) 0.29   0.5

(d) 0.08   0.7

(e) 0.75   0.73

2. Write down the smaller number:

    (a) 0.6   0.2

    (b) 0.49   0.71

    (c) 0.6   0.21

    (d) 0.05   0.4

    (e) 0.1   0.01

Here are some more difficult examples of ordering decimals.

Note: It does not matter how many digits there are because **place value** gives you the order of size.

Examples:

(i) Write the following in order of size, starting with the **smallest**:

0.723   0.237   0.74   0.016   0.8

Method 1

Step 1: Are there any whole numbers?

No. All the numbers have 0 in the **Units** column.

Step 2: Look at the first place of decimals (the **tenths** column).

0.723   0.237   0.74   0.016   0.8

- 0.016 is the smallest number
- 0.237 is the next smallest
- 0.723 and 0.74 come next but we don't yet know which is first
- 0.8 is the largest

Step 3: Look at the second place of decimals (the **hundredths** column) in the two numbers that start with 0.7

0.7**2**3   0.7**4**

0.723 is smaller because 2 hundredths ($\frac{2}{100}$) is smaller than 4 hundredths ($\frac{4}{100}$)

Order: 0.016   0.237   0.723   0.74   0.8

Method 2

U	t	h	th
0	7	2	3
0	2	3	7
0	7	4	
0	0	1	6
0	8		

Step 1: List the numbers in place value columns (do not write down the decimal point).

U	t	h	th
0	7	2	3
0	2	3	7
0	7	4	**0**
0	0	1	6
0	8	**0**	**0**

Step 2: Write a zero wherever there is a gap.

Step 3: Read the figures as if they were whole numbers, then re-write them as in the original question.

Order: 0.016   0.237   0.723   0.74   0.8

(ii) Write the following in order of size, starting with the **largest**:

0.43   1.6   0.25   0.06   14.3

Method 1

Step 1: Are there any numbers greater than 1?

0.43   **1**.6   0.25   0.06   **14**.3

Yes: 1 and 14

●   14.4 is the largest number

●   1.6 is the next largest

Step 2: Look at the first place of decimals (the **tenths** column) of the remaining numbers.

0.**4**3   0.**2**5   0.**0**6

These numbers are already in order of size, largest first.

Order: 14.3   1.6   0.43   0.25   0.06

Method 2

T	U	t	h
	0	4	3
	1	6	
	0	2	5
	0	0	6
1	4	3	

Step 1: List the numbers in place value columns.

T	U	t	h
0	0	4	3
0	1	6	**0**
0	0	2	5
0	0	0	6
1	4	3	**0**

Step 2: Write a zero wherever there is a gap.

Step 3: Ignore the decimal points and read the figures as if they were whole numbers, then re-write them as in the original question.

	1430	160	43	25	6
Order:	14.3	1.6	0.43	0.25	0.06

Exercise 14.3: Ordering decimals (2)

1. Write the following in order of size, starting with the **smallest**:
   (a) 0.5   0.7   0.6
   (b) 0.71   0.74   0.73
   (c) 0.82   0.8   0.87
   (d) 0.6   0.502   0.55
   (e) 0.62   0.70   0.07
   (f) 0.320   0.406   0.5   0.17
   (g) 0.14   0.09   0.25   0.123
   (h) 0.102   0.012   0.21   0.12
   (i) 0.45   0.54   0.054   0.504
   (j) 7.1   0.17   1.07   0.71

2. Write the following in order of size, starting with the **largest**:
   (a) 0.16   0.19   0.15
   (b) 0.68   0.64   0.66
   (c) 0.3   0.29   0.31
   (d) 0.106   0.97   0.2
   (e) 0.201   0.021   0.102
   (f) 0.41   0.17   0.8   0.306
   (g) 0.1   0.09   0.242   0.07
   (h) 0.63   0.36   0.063   0.603
   (i) 0.419   0.194   0.491   0.149
   (j) 21.3   2.13   0.213   213

Writing decimals as fractions

To write a decimal as a fraction, we put the decimal part over a power of 10 (10, 100, 1000, …)

If there is **one** place of decimals, we have **tenths**.

Example: $0.7 = \frac{7}{10}$

If there are **two** places of decimals, we have **hundredths**.

Examples:

(i) $0.53 = \frac{53}{100}$

(ii) $0.09 = \frac{09}{100} = \frac{9}{100}$

If there are **three** places of decimals, we have **thousandths**.

Examples:

(i) $0.329 = \frac{329}{1000}$

(ii) $0.017 = \frac{017}{1000} = \frac{17}{1000}$

(iii) $0.003 = \frac{003}{1000} = \frac{3}{1000}$

If there is a whole number, it is the integer part of a mixed number.

Examples:

(i) $17.3 = 17\frac{3}{10}$

(ii) $5.81 = 5\frac{81}{100}$

Exercise 14.4: Writing decimals as fractions (1)

Write the following decimals as fractions:

1. 0.3 $\frac{3}{10}$
2. 0.61
3. 0.127
4. 0.77
5. 0.707

6. 0.7
7. 4.23
8. 62.83
9. 1.369
10. 8.1

18-4-19 f

✓

Marker

You already know that fractions should always be written in their lowest terms.

In Exercise 14.4, you did not need to do anything about this because the fractions were in their lowest terms to begin with – there was no number that you could divide into both the top and bottom of the fraction an exact number of times (remember, dividing by 1 does not change the numbers).

Usually you should check whether the fraction you have written is in its lowest terms.

Tenths: 10 can be divided by 2 and 5

Ask yourself: Can the top number be divided by 2 or 5?

Examples:

(i) $0.2 = \frac{2}{10}$

        $= \frac{1}{5}$ $2 \div 2 = 1$ and $10 \div 2 = 5$

(ii) $0.5 = \frac{5}{10}$

        $= \frac{1}{2}$ $5 \div 5 = 1$ and $10 \div 5 = 2$

(iii) $0.3 = \frac{3}{10}$ 3 and 10 have no common factors. $\frac{3}{10}$ is already
                                 in its lowest terms.

Hundredths: 100 can be divided by 2, 4, 5 and 25

Ask yourself: Can the top number be divided by 2, 4, 5 or 25?

Note: 100 can also be divided by 10, 20 and 50 but when you write a decimal as a fraction you only need to worry about 2, 4, 5 and 25

Examples:

(i) $0.22 = \frac{22}{100}$

$= \frac{11}{50}$ $22 \div 2 = 11$ and $100 \div 2 = 50$

(ii) $0.28 = \frac{28}{100}$

$= \frac{7}{25}$ $28 \div 4 = 7$ and $100 \div 4 = 25$

(iii) $0.85 = \frac{85}{100}$

$= \frac{17}{20}$ $85 \div 5 = 17$ and $100 \div 5 = 20$

(iv) $0.25 = \frac{25}{100}$

$= \frac{1}{4}$ $25 \div 25 = 1$ and $100 \div 25 = 4$

It is always a good idea to check whether you can divide the top and bottom numbers a second time, in case you could have divided by a larger number than you thought. Let's look at Examples (ii) and (iv) above again.

Examples:

(ii) $0.28 = \frac{28}{100}$

$= \frac{14}{50}$ $28 \div 2 = 14$ and $100 \div 2 = 50$

$= \frac{7}{25}$ $14 \div 2 = 7$ and $50 \div 2 = 25$

(iv) $0.25 = \frac{25}{100}$

$\qquad = \frac{5}{20}$ $\qquad$ $25 \div 5 = 5$ and $100 \div 5 = 20$

$\qquad = \frac{1}{4}$ $\qquad$ $5 \div 5 = 1$ and $20 \div 5 = 4$

Exercise 14.5: Writing decimals as fractions (2)

Write the following decimals as fractions, giving your answers in their lowest terms:

Alasha
19.01.19

1. 0.6
2. 0.8
3. 0.5
4. 0.14
5. 0.12

6. 0.15
7. 0.25
8. 0.18
9. 0.4
10. 0.46

11. 0.16
12. 0.35
13. 0.62
14. 0.44
15. 0.45

16. 0.32
17. 0.74
18. 0.24
19. 0.95
20. 0.75

21. 0.02
22. 0.04
23. 0.05
24. 3.2
25. 1.26

You should try to **learn** these very commonly used fractions and their equivalent decimal number:

- $0.25 = \frac{1}{4}$

- $0.5 = \frac{1}{2}$

- $0.75 = \frac{3}{4}$

- $0.1 = \frac{1}{10}$

So $0.3 = \frac{3}{10}$, $0.7 = \frac{7}{10}$, $0.9 = \frac{9}{10}$

Exercise 14.6: Summary exercise

1. Write down the real value of the underlined digits:

   (a) 26.3<u>9</u>7

   (b) <u>2</u>6.397

   (c) 26.39<u>7</u>

   (d) 26.<u>3</u>97

   (e) 2<u>6</u>.397

2. Write these decimals in order of size, starting with the **largest**:

   (a) 0.86   0.72   0.9   0.75

   (b) 0.313   0.33   0.32   0.033

   (c) 0.759   0.700   1.700   0.790

3. Write these decimals in order of size, starting with the **smallest**:

   (a) 0.53   0.69   0.45   0.96

   (b) 0.426   0.400   0.460   0.004

   (c) 3.51   5.32   3.15   5.23

4. Write these decimals as fractions in their lowest terms:

    (a) 0.6   (e) 0.25

    (b) 0.15   (f) 0.44

    (c) 0.62   (g) 0.08

    (d) 0.5   (h) 0.7

End of chapter activity: Dominoes

Preparation

Cut out the set of dominoes from the worksheet. (It might be a good idea to stick them onto card to make them easier to handle.)

How to play

Once you have cut out your dominoes you are ready to play. The game is for two players.

● Lay all the dominoes face down on the table.

● Each player picks five dominoes. The rest remain face down on the table.

● The player with the largest decimal goes first by placing one of his/her dominoes on the table, face up. (If both players hold the same decimal then the larger fraction on the dominoes decides who plays first.)

● The next player plays a domino with a matching fraction–decimal or a matching decimal–fraction.

For example, if $\boxed{\frac{1}{2} \mid 0.9}$ is played first, the next player needs a domino showing 0.5 (to match the $\frac{1}{2}$) or $\frac{9}{10}$ (to match the 0.9)

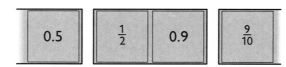

Dominoes can be placed only at either end of the line of dominoes in play. If a player does not hold a matching domino, he/she must forfeit his/her turn and take another domino from those still face down on the table.

● Play continues until one of the players has no dominoes left and calls out 'domino!'.

Did you know?

The average adult body contains roughly 5 litres of blood.

Chapter 15: Decimal addition and subtraction

We have already learnt the formal methods of addition and subtraction. The numbers must be set out in columns according to their place value: **Units** go under **Units**, **Tens** under **Tens**, and so on.

We add and subtract decimals in exactly the same way, and it is easy to put the numbers in the correct columns: you just need to **keep the point under the point**.

Adding decimals

Examples:

(i)   3.74 + 5.61

	U	·	t	h
	3	·	7	4
+	5	·	6	1
	9	·	3	5
	1			

(ii)   6.4 + 12.3 + 8.75

	T	U	·	t	h
		6	·	4	
+	1	2	·	3	
		8	·	7	5
	2	7	·	4	5
	1	1			

(iii)   0.97 + 97 + 9.7

97 is the same as 97.00

	H	T	U	·	t	h
			0	·	9	7
+		9	7	·		
			9	·	7	
	1	0	7	·	6	7
		1	1			

Exercise 15.1 : Adding decimals

Calculate the following:

1.

U	t	h
6 · 3		
+ 2 · 5		
·		

2.

U	t	h
2 · 4		
+ 5 · 9		
·		

3.

U	t	h
8 · 3		
+ 9 · 6		
·		

4. 6.7 + 8.5

5. 42.3 + 16.1

6. 15.7 + 72.8

7. 83.6 + 65.2

8. 28.7 + 19.6

9. 49.5 + 54.8

10. 78.6 + 49.6

11. 1.7 + 0.8 + 9.2

12. 8.4 + 1.8 + 6.7

13. 4.7 + 2.5 + 6.3

14. 8.9 + 7.6 + 9.8

15. 0.7 + 0.6 + 0.9

16. 2.46 + 3.72 + 4.37

17. 5.34 + 4.53 + 3.45

18. 42.3 + 19.7 + 34.6

19. 38.7 + 29.4 + 17.6

20. 36.7 + 18.9 + 27.1

21. 3.46 + 27.2

22. 47.3 + 2.98

23. 8.75 + 2.9

24. 1.7 + 3.86

25. 2.6 + 0.735

26. 24 + 8.6

27. 27.3 + 45

28. 9 + 3.75

29. 7.6 + 28

30. 2.83 + 49

31. 41.6 + 2.8 + 1.43

32. 24.2 + 18.8 + 1.75

33. 1.86 + 4.9 + 32.4

34. 17.4 + 1.74 + 0.174

35. 4.36 + 43.6 + 0.436

36. 27 + 1.4 + 36.6

37. 1.37 + 12 + 1.82

38. 1.4 + 0.4 + 14

39. 125 + 7.8 + 48.4

40. 50.3 + 503 + 5.03

Subtracting decimals

When setting out the calculation, remember:

- Keep the point under the point.

- A whole number can be written with a decimal point at the end.

You can check your answer by adding the bottom two lines together. They should equal the top line.

Examples:

(i) 46.3 − 18.9

T	U ·	t	h
³4̸	¹⁵6̸ ·	¹3	
− 1	8 ·	9	
2	7 ·	4	

Step 1: You can't take 9 away from 3, so take 1 unit from the **Units** column. Now 13 − 9 = 4

Step 2: You can't take 8 away from 5, so take 1 ten from the **Tens** column. Now you have 15 − 8 = 7

Step 3: Finally 3 − 1 = 2

Check: 27.4 + 18.9 = 46.3 ✓

(ii) 31.6 − 7.8

T	U ·	t	h
²3̸	¹⁰1̸ ·	¹6	
−	7 ·	8	
2	3 ·	8	

Check: 23.8 + 7.8 = 31.6 ✓

(iii) 26.3 − 1.86

T	U·t	h
2	⁵6·³⁄ᵗ⁷²3	¹0
−	1·8	6
2	4·4	4

Tip: Fill any gaps in the **top** line with **0**s

Check: 24.44 + 1.86 = 26.3 ✓

(iv) 24 − 1.39

T	U·t	h
2	³4·⁹⁄ᵗ⁷0	¹0
−	1·3	9
2	2·6	1

Note: Here you have to go to the **Units** column to take 1 unit, first into the tenths column and then to the hundredths column

Check: 22.61 + 1.39 = 24 ✓

Exercise 15.2: Subtracting decimals

Calculate the following:

1. 4.6 − 1.2
2. 7.3 − 2.9
3. 8.4 − 7.8
4. 2.46 − 1.28
5. 7.59 − 2.74

6. 8.64 − 1.97
7. 73.6 − 41.9
8. 82.5 − 57.3
9. 34.3 − 17.6
10. 41.8 − 32.6

11. 7.51 − 0.86
12. 40.8 − 12.6
13. 6.08 − 1.95
14. 30.5 − 17.8
15. 9.02 − 6.29

16. 3.86 − 1.9
17. 27.3 − 2.4
18. 7.6 − 4.28
19. 2.4 − 1.33
20. 4.6 − 0.454

21. 24.6 − 3.42

22. 93.6 − 1.97

23. 81.3 − 3.86

24. 14.3 − 8.76

25. 2.48 − 0.638

26. 76 − 4.2

27. 74 − 7.4

28. 32.3 − 0.122

29. 19 − 1.37

30. 34 − 0.76

31. 6 − 0.47

32. 0.5 − 0.136

33. 374 − 7.86

34. 258 − 25.8

35. 2 − 0.371

Exercise 15.3: Summary exercise

1. (a) Calculate 4.37 + 2.96

   (b) Add together 14.8, 2.97 and 9.5

   (c) What is the total of 1.8 plus 27 plus 24.3?

   (d) Increase 19.8 by 6.7

   (e) What is the sum of 4.63 and 46.3?

2. (a) Calculate 45.3 − 28.6

   (b) Subtract 4.83 from 38.6

   (c) By how much is 42.5 larger than 8.7?

   (d) What must be added to 8.65 to make 15?

   (e) What is the difference between 85 and 8.5?

3. Calculate:

(a) 3.7 + 5.9 − 4.8

(b) 7.5 − 3.8 + 1.7

(c) 8 − 2.6 + 3.7

(d) 7.2 − 2.8 − 1.6

(e) 1.67 − 0.85 + 7.58

(f) 45.6 + 87.7 − 58.7

(g) 12.8 + 6.32 − 9.7

(h) 17.3 − 9.86 + 8.9

(i) 8.6 + 12 − 1.63

(j) 24.6 + 7.56 − 8.7

End of chapter activity: Missing digits (division) ▢

These calculations are **divisions**. An asterisk (*) represents a missing digit.

Re-write the sums without any digits missing.

1.
	*	4	
2	6	*	

6.
		4	*
*	2	5	8

2.
	3	2	
*	9	*	

7.
		*	0
9	3	*	0

3.
		3	7
*	1	*	5

8.
		*	*
7	5	*	7

4.
		*	1
*	4	0	8

9.
		4	*
3	*	*	9

5.
		7	2
4	*	*	8

10.
	1	9	7
5	*	*	*

Did you know?

When at rest, the average adult heart beats 70 times per minute.

This means it beats: 4200 times every hour

100 800 times every day

705 600 times every week

36 792 000 times every year

How many times might your heart beat in your lifetime?

Chapter 16: Scales, estimation and rounding

You already know how to read numbers off, and write them on, a scale. Now we are going to look at scales that go up higher than those you have met before, and at scales involving decimal numbers.

Reading scales

Remember, the first thing we must **always** do is work out what one **division** (mark) means.

Examples:

What numbers are the arrows pointing at?

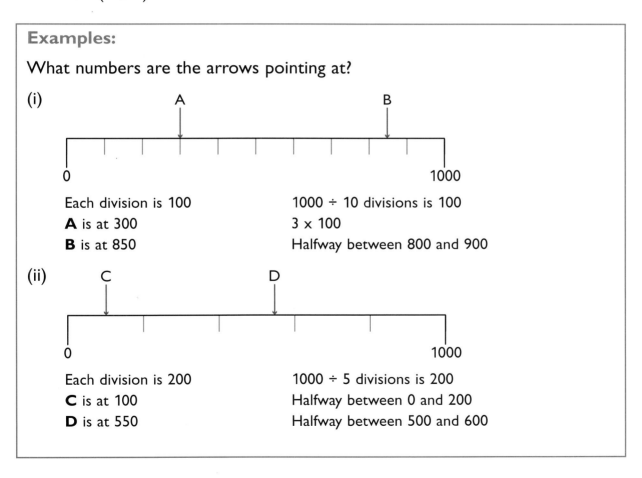

(i)

Each division is 100   1000 ÷ 10 divisions is 100
A is at 300   3 × 100
B is at 850   Halfway between 800 and 900

(ii)

Each division is 200   1000 ÷ 5 divisions is 200
C is at 100   Halfway between 0 and 200
D is at 550   Halfway between 500 and 600

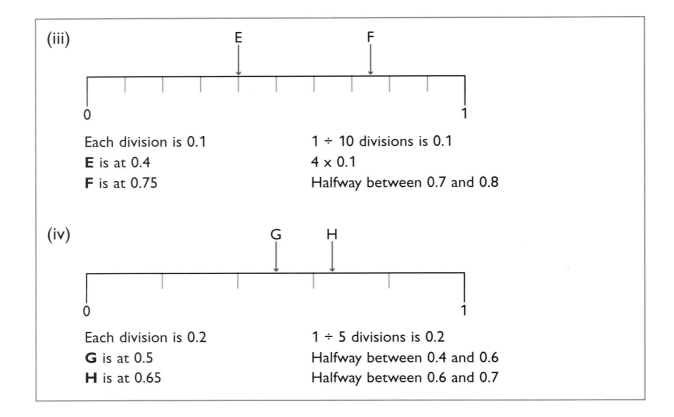

(iii)

Each division is 0.1   1 ÷ 10 divisions is 0.1
E is at 0.4   4 x 0.1
F is at 0.75   Halfway between 0.7 and 0.8

(iv)

Each division is 0.2   1 ÷ 5 divisions is 0.2
G is at 0.5   Halfway between 0.4 and 0.6
H is at 0.65   Halfway between 0.6 and 0.7

Exercise 16.1: Reading scales

Write down the numbers that the arrows A, B and C are pointing at:

1.

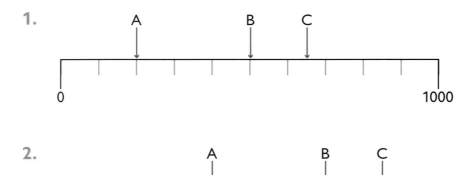

2.

3.

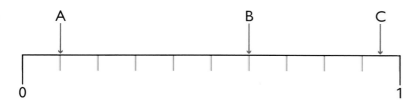

4.

5.

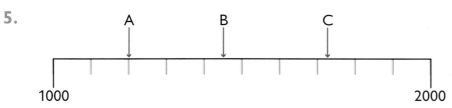

6.

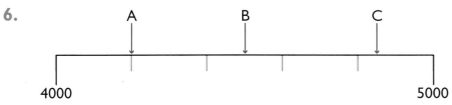

7.

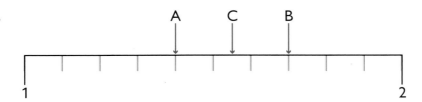

8.

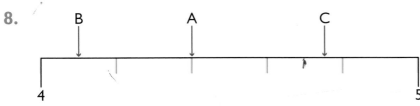

Marking numbers on a scale

Remember, when marking a number on a scale it is useful to work out the halfway mark and then halve the halves to find where the quarter marks are. If it is an accurate scale, a ruler might help. If the scale is drawn on squared paper, you can also use the grid lines to help you.

Examples:

Mark the numbers **A**, **B** and **C** with arrows on the number lines below:

(i)   **A** = 300, **B** = 900 and **C** = 750

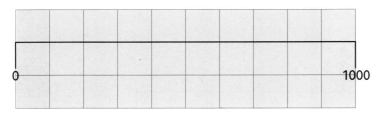

$\frac{1}{2}$ of 1000 is 500   Mark it at halfway (see diagram below)

Look at the grid lines on the squared paper. There are **10** divisions.

Each division is 100 (1000 ÷ 10 = 100)

A (300) is two squares less than 500
B (900) is one square less than 1000
C (750) is halfway between 500 and 1000

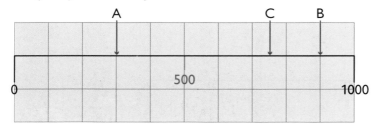

(ii)   **A** = 250, **B** = 400 and **C** = 800

$\frac{1}{2}$ of 1000 is 500 — Mark it at halfway (see diagram below)

$\frac{1}{2}$ of 500 is 250 — Mark 250 and 750

A (250) is already marked
B (400) is between 250 and 500 but nearer to 500
C (800) is between 750 and 1000 but nearer to 750

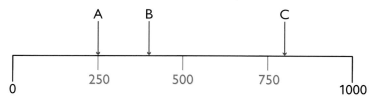

(iii) **A** = 0.1, **B** = 0.8 and **C** = 0.25

$\frac{1}{2}$ of 1 is 0.5 — Mark it at halfway

Look at the grid lines on the squared paper. There are 10 divisions.

Each division is 0.1 ($1 \div 10 = 0.1$)

A (0.1) is one square greater than 0
B (0.8) is two squares less than 1
C (0.25) is halfway between 0 and 0.5

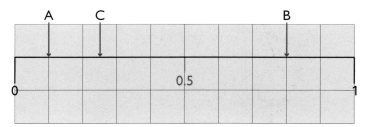

(iv) **A** = 0.75, **B** = 0.6 and **C** = 0.2

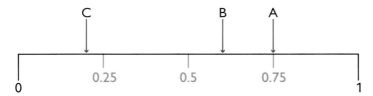

$\frac{1}{2}$ of 1 is 0.5   Mark it at halfway

$\frac{1}{2}$ of 0.5 is 0.25   Mark 0.25 and 0.75

A (0.75) is already marked
B (0.6) is between 0.5 and 0.75 but nearer to 0.5
C (0.2) is between 0 and 0.25 but nearer to 0.25

Exercise 16.2:
Marking numbers on a scale

Copy the scales below and mark the numbers A, B, and C with arrows:

1. A = 500, B = 900 and C = 350

2. A = 400, B = 700 and C = 150

3. A = 500, B = 250 and C = 800

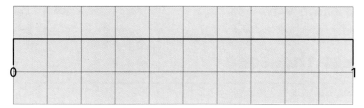

0   1000

4. A = 300, B = 600 and C = 750

0   1000

5. A = 0.5, B = 0.1 and C = 0.65

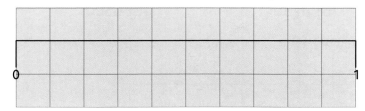

0   1

6. A = 0.2, B = 0.7 and C = 0.85

0   1

7. A = 0.5, B = 0.25 and C = 0.9

0   1

8. A = 0.3, B = 0.6 and C = 0.75

0   1

Rounding numbers

You already know how to round numbers to the nearest 10 and to the nearest 100

Remember: If a number falls **below the halfway mark** it is **rounded down**.

If a number falls **at** or **above the halfway mark** it is **rounded up**.

Rounding to the nearest 1000 or to the nearest whole number works in exactly the same way.

Rounding to the nearest thousand

Example:

Write each of these numbers to the nearest 1000:

(a) 6400   (b) 6750   (c) 6500

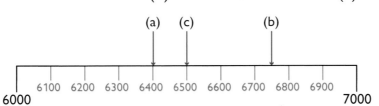

All three numbers are between 6000 and 7000 (6500 is the halfway point).

From the diagram you can see that:

(a)   6400 is less than 6500 and therefore nearer to **6000** than 7000

So we can say that 6400 written to the nearest thousand is 6000

(b)   6750 is more than 6500 and therefore nearer to **7000** than 6000

So we can say that 6750 written to the nearest thousand is 7000

(c)   6500 is exactly halfway between 6000 and 7000 but we **always** round up if a number is exactly at the halfway point.

So we can say that 6500 written to the nearest thousand is 7000

Exercise 16.3: Rounding to the nearest 1000

1. Write these numbers to the nearest 1000:

   (a) 2600   (b) 4300   (c) 7150   (d) 8498   (e) 1500

2. The Nile is 4187 miles long. What is the length of the river to the nearest 1000 miles?

3. Mr Tempest polled 7748 votes. How many votes did he receive to the nearest 1000?

4. Mount Everest is 8850 metres high. Write this height to the nearest 1000 metres.

5. The number of days in a decade is 3653
   Write this number of days to the nearest 1000

6. Ali buys a second hand car for £5895

   How much, to the nearest £1000, did Ali pay?

7. Farmer Delight has 3196 turkeys. How many turkeys does he have to the nearest 1000?

8. The village of Upper Binding has a population of 1863
   What is the population to the nearest 1000?

9. There are 8760 hours in a year. How many is this written to the nearest 1000?

10. Last year Pamela drove exactly 9500 miles. How far did she drive to the nearest 1000 miles?

Rounding to the nearest whole number

Example:

Write each of these numbers to the nearest whole number:

(a) 4.3   (b) 4.85   (c) 4.5

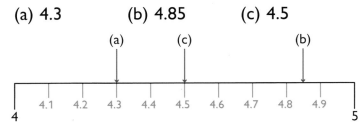

All three numbers are between 4 and 5 (4.5 is the halfway point).

From the diagram you can see that:

(a)   4.3 is less than 4.5 and therefore nearer to **4** than 5

So we can say that 4.3 written to the nearest whole number is 4

(b)   4.85 is more than 4.5 and therefore nearer to **5** than 4

So we can say that 4.85 written to the nearest whole number is 5

(c)   4.5 is exactly halfway between 4 and 5 but we **always** round up if a number is exactly at the halfway point.

So we can say that 4.5 written to the nearest whole number is 5

Exercise 16.4: Rounding to the nearest whole number

1.   Write these numbers to the nearest whole number:

(a) 8.7   (b) 7.4   (c) 3.19   (d) 5.85   (e) 2.5

2.   A chicken has mass 2.8 kilograms. What is the mass to the nearest kilogram?

3.   The temperature is 7.3 °C. What is the temperature to the nearest degree?

4. Joyce ran **100** metres in **10.9** seconds. Round this time to the nearest second.

5. In the high jump Galina cleared the bar at **2.09** metres. What is this height to the nearest metre?

6. Johan spent **£27.45** on a birthday present for his sister. How much did he spend to the nearest pound?

7. Dan measured his pet snake to be **48.6** centimetres long. How long is the snake to the nearest centimetre?

8. Normal human body temperature is **36.9** °C, or **98.4** °F. Write each temperature to the nearest degree.

9. On average Gladys drinks **8.45** cups of tea each day. How many cups of tea does she drink each day to the nearest whole number?

10. Ron is **123.5** centimetres tall. How tall is he to the nearest centimetre?

· ·

Exercise 16.5: Summary exercise

1. Write down the numbers that the arrows A, B and C are pointing at:

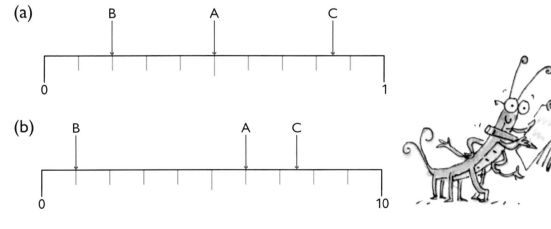

(a)

(b)

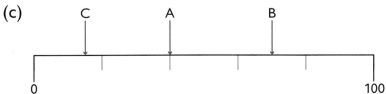

(c)

(d)

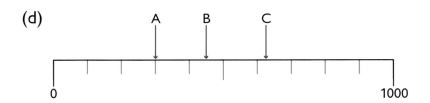

(e)

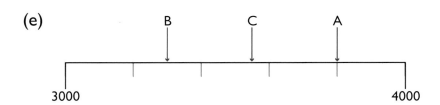

(f)

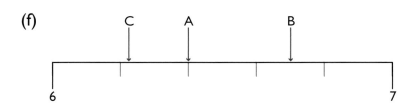

2. Copy the scales below and mark the numbers A, B, and C with arrows:

(a) A = 0.6, B = 0.75 and C = 0.25

(b) A = 0.5, B = 0.4 and C = 0.2

(c) A = 1, B = 6 and C = 8.5

(d) A = 5, B = 7 and C = 2.5

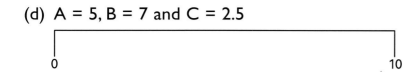

0   10

(e) A = 20, B = 60 and C = 85

0   100

(f) A = 50, B = 75 and C = 10

0   100

(g) A = 300, B = 800 and C = 450

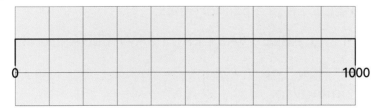

0   1000

(h) A = 500, B = 250 and C = 750

0   1000

3. Write the following to the nearest whole number:

    (a) 4.6   (b) 3.4   (c) 7.5   (d) 9.86

4. Write the following as numbers to the nearest 10:

    (a) 38   (b) 74   (c) 81   (d) 15

5. Write the following numbers to the nearest 100:

    (a) 128   (b) 463   (c) 850   (d) 290

6. Write the following numbers to the nearest 1000:

    (a) 7824   (b) 6198   (c) 8510   (d) 3500

End of chapter activity: Palindromes

A **palindrome** is a word or sentence which reads the same backwards as it does forwards:

- MUM, MINIM and REDDER are palindromes.

- MADAM I'M ADAM and ABLE WAS I ERE I SAW ELBA are also palindromes.

Numbers can be palindromes also:

- 33, 121, 1001 and so on.

Here is a way of finding lots of palindromes.

- Take any 2-digit number.

- Copy the 2-digit number.

- Reverse the digits.

- Add the two numbers.

- Continue reversing and adding until you get a palindrome.

Examples:

A palindrome in one stage:

4	5
5	4
9	9

A palindrome in two stages:

	2	8
	8	2
1	1	0
0	1	1
1	2	1

Choose some 2-digit numbers and see how many stages it takes you to get to a palindrome. (Be sensible and stop if it is taking you too many stages!)

Did you know?

When Nelson Mandela, who later became President of the Republic of South Africa, was imprisoned on Robben Island his prison number was 46664 – another palindrome.

Chapter 17: Multiplication and division by 10, 100 and 1000

You already know how to multiply and divide whole numbers by 10, 100 and 1000

In this chapter we are going to look at what happens when the calculations involve decimal numbers.

Multiplication by 10, 100 and 1000

So far you have only multiplied whole numbers by 10, 100 and 1000

When we **multiply by 10**, the digits move **1 place to the left**.

Examples:

(i) | 3 | 9 | × | 1 | 0 | = | 3 | 9 | 0 |

(ii) | 1 | 4 | 5 | × | 1 | 0 | = | 1 | 4 | 5 | 0 |

When we **multiply by 100**, the digits move **2 places to the left**.

Examples:

(i) | 4 | × | 1 | 0 | 0 | = | 4 | 0 | 0 |

(ii) | 6 | 0 | 2 | × | 1 | 0 | 0 | = | 6 | 0 | 2 | 0 | 0 |

When we **multiply by 1000**, the digits move **3 places to the left**.

Examples:

(i) | 8 | × | 1 | 0 | 0 | 0 | = | 8 | 0 | 0 | 0 |

(ii) | 4 | 0 | × | 1 | 0 | 0 | 0 | = | 4 | 0 | 0 | 0 | 0 |

Exercise 17.1: Multiplying whole numbers by 10, 100 and 1000

Calculate the following:

1. 7 x 10
2. 46 x 10
3. 804 x 10
4. 1070 x 10
5. 6 x 100

6. 49 x 100
7. 300 x 100
8. 1234 x 100
9. 9 x 1000
10. 37 x 1000

11. 716 x 1000
12. 1000 x 1000
13. 47 x 100
14. 38 x 10
15. 500 x 10

16. 72 x 1000
17. 7 x 100
18. 2 x 1000
19. 2000 x 100
20. 125 x 10

When you multiply decimals **the rules do not change**. The digits 'jump over' the decimal point.

When we **multiply by 10**, the digits move **1 place to the left**.

Examples:

(i) | 3 · 6 | x | 1 | 0 | = | 3 | 6 | Whole number 36

(ii) | 0 · 7 | x | 1 | 0 | = | 0 | 7 | Whole number 7

(iii) | 4 · 2 | 5 | x | 1 | 0 | = | 4 | 2 · 5 |

(iv) | 0 · 3 | 7 | 5 | x | 1 | 0 | = | 0 | 3 · 7 | 5 | Write this as 3.75

Note: Sometimes there are not enough digits to 'jump over' the decimal point, but we can add extra 0s at the end of a decimal number (after the decimal point) without altering the size of the number.

14.6 = 14.60 = 14.600 and so on.

When we **multiply by 100**, the digits move **2 places to the left**.

Examples:

(i)

| 2 | 1·7 | 5 | × | 1 | 0 | 0 | = | 2 | 1 | 7 | 5 |

Whole number 2175

(ii)

| 0·8 | 6 | 2 | × | 1 | 0 | 0 | = | 0 | 8 | 6·2 |

Write this as 86.2

(iii)

| 1 | 4·6 | (0) | × | 1 | 0 | 0 | = | 1 | 4 | 6 | 0 |

Extra 0 needed.

When we **multiply by 1000**, the digits move **3 places to the left**.

Examples:

(i)   0.0625 × 1000 = 0062.5   Write this as 62.5

(ii) 3.86(0) × 1000 = 3860   Extra 0 needed to give whole number 3860

(iii) 0.4(00) × 1000 = 0400   Extra 0s needed to give whole number 400

Exercise 17.2: Multiplying decimals by 10, 100 and 1000

1. Multiply these numbers by 10:

    (a) 4.3   (c) 0.19

    (b) 28.64   (d) 0.8

2. Multiply these numbers by 100:

    (a) 4.632   (d) 0.0423

    (b) 3.86   (e) 0.0016

    (c) 0.872   (f) 1.7

3. Multiply these numbers by 1000:

    (a) 1.295   (e) 0.4

    (b) 0.3267   (f) 23.42

    (c) 12.329   (g) 0.24

    (d) 0.087   (h) 0.365

4. Calculate the following:

(a) 1.75 × 10 *1*

(b) 3.38 × 100 *2*

(c) 2.55 × 1000 *3*

(d) 0.8 × 10 *1*

(e) 0.07 × 10 *)*

(f) 72.93 × 100 *× 2*

(g) 1.425 × 100 *2*

(h) 0.345 × 1000 *3*

(i) 0.96 × 1000 *3*

(j) 0.14 × 10 *1*

(k) 0.01 × 1000 *3*

(l) 0.001 × 1000 *3*

(m) 27.2 × 100 *2*

(n) 0.06 × 10 *1*

(o) 7.05 × 1000 *3*

(p) 8.4 × 100 *2*

(q) 38.75 × 10 *1*

(r) 2.6 × 1000 *3*

(s) 0.295 × 100 *2*

(t) 0.405 × 10 *1*

Division by 10, 100 and 1000

So far, when you have divided by 10, 100 and 1000, the answer has always been a whole number.

When we **divide by 10**, the digits move **1 place to the right**.

Examples:

(i)   420 ÷ 10 = 42

(ii)   6000 ÷ 10 = 600

When we **divide by 100**, the digits move **2 places to the right**.

Examples:

(i)   9000 ÷ 100 = 90

(ii)   75 000 ÷ 100 = 750

When we **divide by 1000**, the digits move **3 places to the right**.

> **Examples:**
>
> (i) $6000 \div 1000 = 6$
>
> (ii) $430\,000 \div 1000 = 430$

Exercise 17.3: Dividing by 10, 100 and 1000 (whole number answers)

Calculate the following:

1. $70 \div 10$
2. $120 \div 10$
3. $8000 \div 10$
4. $400 \div 100$
5. $8000 \div 100$

6. $43\,000 \div 100$
7. $2000 \div 1000$
8. $38\,000 \div 1000$
9. $120\,000 \div 1000$
10. $1\,000\,000 \div 1000$

The answer to a division can be a decimal number. As for multiplication, **the rules do not change**. The digits 'jump over' the decimal point, but this time to the right.

Remember: All whole numbers could be written with a decimal point at the right-hand end.

    8 is the same as 8.0
    27 is the same as 27.0
    400 is the same as 400.0
    and so on

When we **divide by 10**, the digits move **1 place to the right**.

> **Examples:**
>
> (i) $34 \div 10 = 3.4$
>
> (ii) $125 \div 10 = 12.5$
>
> (iii) $4.8 \div 10 = 0.48$ Always put a 0 in the **Units** column. Do not write .48

Note: Sometimes there are not enough digits to 'jump over' the decimal point, but we can add extra 0s at the beginning of a number (before the decimal point) without altering the size of the number.

$3 = 03 = 003$ and so on.

When we **divide by 100**, the digits move **2 places to the right**.

Examples:

(i) $250 \div 100 = 2.50$ Write this as 2.5

(ii) $68 \div 100 = 0.68$ Remember the 0 in the **Units** column.

(iii) $(0)3 \div 100 = 0.03$ Extra 0 needed. Remember the 0 in the **Units** column.

When we **divide by 1000**, the digits move **3 places to the right**.

Examples:

(i) $7240 \div 1000 = 7.240$ Write this as 7.24

(ii) $280 \div 1000 = 0.280$ Remember the 0 in the **Units** column and write this as 0.28

(iii) $(00)8 \div 1000 = 0.008$ Extra 0s needed. Remember the 0 in the **Units** column.

Exercise 17.4: Dividing by 10, 100 and 1000 (decimal answers)

1.   Divide these numbers by 10:

   (a) 18.6 1.86

   (b) 6.3

   (c) 19   1.9

   (d) 835

   (e) 2300   230.00

   (f) 3

2. Divide these numbers by 100:

   (a) 148.2 *1.482*   (e) 15 130

   (b) 38.7   (f) 62

   (c) 1700 *17.000* (g) 6.4

   (d) 365   (h) 9

3. Divide these numbers by 1000:

   (a) 4865.   (e) 425

   (b) 27 900 *27.9000* (f) 5

   (c) 787.5   (g) 18.4

   (d) 2500 *2.5000* (h) 7.2

4. Calculate the following:

   (a) 32.4 ÷ 10   (g) 2874 ÷ 100 *2*

   (b) 123.4 ÷ 100 *21.234*   (h) 7.8 ÷ 10 *1*

   (c) 3217.9 ÷ 1000 *3*   (i) 83 ÷ 100 *2*

   (d) 298 ÷ 10 *29.80*   (j) 409 ÷ 1000 *3*

   (e) 350 ÷ 100 *2*   (k) 6 ÷ 10

   (f) 2756 ÷ 1000 *2.756*   (l) 500 ÷ 1000

   (m) 28.4 ÷ 100   (s) 0.09 ÷ 10

   (n) 6 ÷ 100   (t) 0.2 ÷ 1000

   (o) 1.5 ÷ 1000   (u) 0.27 ÷ 10

   (p) 0.8 ÷ 100   (v) 0.04 ÷ 100

   (q) 35.5 ÷ 1000   (w) 7 ÷ 1000

   (r) 4.6 ÷ 100   (x) 0.1 ÷ 10

Exercise 17.5: Summary exercise

Calculate the following:

1. 65 x 10
2. 0.7 x 10
3. 45.32 x 10
4. 0.065 x 10
5. 9.45 x 10

6. 10 x 100
7. 2.86 x 100
8. 0.7 x 100
9. 4.915 x 100
10. 307 x 100

11. 70 x 1000
12. 0.875 x 1000
13. 4.34 x 1000
14. 0.01 x 1000
15. 28.9 x 1000

16. 33 ÷ 10
17. 4.26 ÷ 10
18. 876 ÷ 10
19. 7 ÷ 10
20. 0.06 ÷ 10

21. 5780 ÷ 100
22. 173.7 ÷ 100
23. 27 ÷ 100
24. 1 ÷ 100
25. 250 ÷ 100

26. 1247 ÷ 1000
27. 23.8 ÷ 1000
28. 9 ÷ 1000
29. 246.95 ÷ 1000
30. 0.23 ÷ 1000

End of chapter activity: Mrs Chick

Mrs Chick collects some eggs which she puts into some baskets.

If she puts 7 eggs in each basket she has one egg left over.

If she puts 9 eggs in each basket she has one basket left with no eggs in it.

How many baskets are there and how many eggs did Mrs Chick collect?

Clue: Think first of multiples of 7 and 9. It might also help you to know that there are less than 50 eggs and less than 6 baskets.

Did you know?

Oxford University is the oldest university in the English-speaking world. Its roots stem from at least the end of the eleventh century.

The King's School, Canterbury, claims to be the oldest existing school, founded in 597 when St. Augustine built an abbey in the school grounds where teaching took place.

Chapter 18: Metric measurement

You already know some of the units we use for **length**, **mass** and **capacity** (**volume**) and how to convert between them. In this chapter we are going to revise these units, and learn about some more.

Length

These are the most common units of length:

        10 **millimetres** (mm) = 1 centimetre (cm)
        100 **centimetres** (cm) = 1 metre (m)
        1000 millimetres (mm) = 1 metre (m)
        1000 **metres** (m)   = 1 kilometre (km)

When we change a **larger** unit of length into a **smaller** one, we **multiply**. This is because we will have **more** of the smaller unit than we did of the larger one (imagine changing £3 into pence: 3 x 100 = 300p).

Centimetres to millimetres

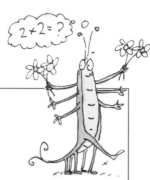

1 cm = 10 mm, so multiply the number of centimetres by 10

Examples:

(i)   6 cm = 6 x 10 mm = 60 mm

(ii)   8.5 cm = 8.5 x 10 mm = 85 mm

Metres to centimetres

1 m = 100 cm, so multiply the number of metres by 100

Examples:

(i)   4 m = 4 x 100 cm = 400 cm

(ii)   12.5 m = 12.5 x 100 cm = 1250 cm

Metres to millimetres

1 m = 1000 mm, so multiply the number of metres by 1000

Examples:

(i)   2 m = 2 x 1000 = 2000 mm

(ii)   0.8 m = 0.8 x 1000 = 800 mm

Kilometres to metres

1 km = 1000 m, so multiply the number of kilometres by 1000

Examples:

(i)   15 km = 15 x 1000 m = 15 000 m

(ii)   2.4 km = 2.4 x 1000 m = 2400 m

Exercise 18.1: Converting length (1)

1. Write the following in millimetres:

(a) 8 cm   (d) 3.25 cm

(b) 15 cm   (e) 0.5 cm

(c) 6.8 cm

2. Write the following in centimetres:

(a) 2 m   (d) 1.3 m

(b) 15 m   (e) 0.5 m

(c) 4.75 m

3. Write the following in millimetres:

(a) 3 m   (d) 2.7 m

(b) 10 m   (e) 0.5 m

(c) 1.25 m

4. Write the following in metres:

   (a) 8 km

   (b) 25 km

   (c) 4.75 km

   (d) 7.9 km

   (e) 0.5 km

5. Write the following in the unit shown in brackets:

   (a) 7 cm   (mm)

   (b) 3 km   (m)

   (c) 6 m   (cm)

   (d) 6 m   (mm)

   (e) 8.8 cm   (mm)

   (f) 4.3 m   (cm)

   (g) 0.85 m   (cm)

   (h) 11.6 km   (m)

   (i) 0.75 m   (mm)

   (j) 12 cm   (mm)

When we change a **smaller** unit of length into a **larger** one, we **divide**. This is because we will have **less** of the larger unit than we did of the smaller one (imagine changing 600p into pounds: 600 ÷ 100 = £6).

Millimetres to centimetres

10 mm = 1 cm, so divide the number of millimetres by 10

Examples:

(i)   70 mm = 70 ÷ 10 cm = 7 cm

(ii)   45 mm = 45 ÷ 10 cm = 4.5 cm

Centimetres to metres

100 cm = 1 m, so divide the number of centimetres by 100

Examples:

(i)   900 cm = 900 ÷ 100 m = 9 m

(ii)   80 cm = 80 ÷ 100 m = 0.8 m

Millimetres to metres

1000 mm = 1m, so divide the number of millimetres by 1000

Examples:

(i)   1600 mm = 1600 ÷ 1000 m = 1.6 m

(ii)   440 mm = 440 ÷ 1000 m = 0.440 m

Metres to kilometres

1000 m = 1 km, so divide the number of metres by 1000

Examples:

(i)   15 000 m = 15 000 ÷ 1000 km = 15 km

(ii)   55 m = 55 ÷ 1000 km = 0.055 km

Exercise 18.2: Converting length (2)

1. Write the following in centimetres:

(a) 60 mm   (c) 300 mm

(b) 38 mm   (d) 8 mm

2. Write the following in metres:

(a) 700 cm   (c) 30 cm

(b) 1250 cm   (d) 7 cm

3. Write the following in metres:

(a) 9000 mm   (c) 750 mm

(b) 5500 mm   (d) 85 mm

4. Write the following in kilometres:

(a) 3000 m   (c) 400 m

(b) 25 000 m   (d) 110 m

5. Write the following in the unit shown in brackets:

   (a) 25 cm   (m)   (f) 1270 mm (m)

   (b) 12 000 m (km)   (g) 80 m   (km)

   (c) 745 mm   (m)   (h) 280 cm   (m)

   (d) 75 mm   (cm)   (i) 1 mm   (cm)

   (e) 1500 m   (km)   (j) 1 cm   (m)

Mass

These are the most common units of mass:

> 1000 **milligrams** (mg) = 1 gram (g)
> 1000 **grams** (g) = 1 kilogram (kg)
> 1000 **kilograms** (kg) = 1 metric tonne (t)

Each of these units is equal to 1000 smaller units. This means that when you convert between them, you will always multiply or divide by **1000**

As with length, when we change a **larger** unit of length into a **smaller** one, we **multiply**.

   1 g = 1000 mg   1 kg = 1000 g   1 t = 1000 kg

so to convert

   grams to milligrams   kilograms to grams   tonnes to kilograms

multiply the number of grams/kilograms/tonnes by 1000

Examples:

(i)   12 g = 12 x 1000 mg = 12 000 mg

(ii)   7.5 kg = 7.5 x 1000 g = 7500 g

(iii)   0.45 t = 0.45 x 1000 kg = 450 kg

Exercise 18.3: Converting mass (1)

1. Write the following in milligrams:

   (a) 2 g

   (b) 12 g

   (c) 3.5 g

   (d) 0.6 g

2. Write the following in grams:

   (a) 6 kg

   (b) 14.2 kg

   (c) 0.8 kg

   (d) 5.35 kg

3. Write the following in kilograms:

   (a) 3 t

   (b) 6.7 t

   (c) 0.25 t

   (d) 12 t

4. Write the following in the unit shown in brackets:

   (a) 6 g   (mg)

   (b) 8 kg   (g)

   (c) 15 t   (kg)

   (d) 2.75 kg   (g)

   (e) 7.125 t   (kg)

   (f) 0.6 kg   (g)

   (g) 1.7 t   (kg)

   (h) 10.5 g   (mg)

   (i) 0.385 kg   (g)

   (j) 0.08 t   (kg)

When we change a **smaller** unit of length into a **larger** one, we **divide**.

The connection between the units of mass is always 1000, so you will need to divide the number of milligrams/grams/kilograms by 1000

Examples:

(i)   8000 mg = 8000 ÷ 1000 g = 8 g

(ii)   16 580 g = 16 580 ÷ 1000 kg = 16.580 kg

(iii)   780 kg = 780 ÷ 1000 t = 0.780 t

Exercise 18.4: Converting mass (2)

1. Write the following in grams:

   (a) 6000 mg

   (b) 3700 mg

   (c) 12 000 mg

   (d) 950 mg

2. Write the following in kilograms:

   (a) 2000 g

   (b) 575 g

   (c) 1400 g

   (d) 50g

3. Write the following in tonnes:

   (a) 3000 kg

   (b) 1020 kg

   (c) 700 kg

   (d) 120 000 kg

4. Write the following in the unit shown in the brackets:

   (a) 9000 kg   (t)

   (b) 1200 g   (kg)

   (c) 15 000 mg (g)

   (d) 5050 kg   (t)

   (e) 454 g   (kg)

   (f) 1850 mg   (g)

   (g) 400 kg   (t)

   (h) 50 kg   (t)

   (i) 100 g   (kg)

   (j) 10 mg   (g)

Capacity

There is only one relationship you need to know for capacity:

   1000 **millilitres** (*ml*) = 1 **litre** (*l*)

If you were happy with the conversions of mass, you will have no problems here. Once again we use 1000 every time.

Litres to millilitres

$1 \; l = 1000 \; ml$, so multiply the number of litres by 1000

> **Examples:**
>
> (i) $3.5 \; l = 3.5 \times 1000 \; ml = 3500 \; ml$
>
> (ii) $0.4 \; l = 0.4 \times 1000 \; ml = 400 \; ml$

Millilitres to litres

$1000 \; ml = 1 \; l$, so divide the number of millilitres by 1000

> **Examples:**
>
> (i) $30 \; 000 \; ml = 30 \; 000 \div 1000 \; l = 30 \; l$
>
> (ii) $150 \; ml = 150 \div 1000 \; l = 0.150 \; l$

Exercise 18.5: Converting capacity

1. Write the following in millilitres:

   (a) $5 \; l$ (c) $0.33 \; l$

   (b) $7.5 \; l$ (d) $12 \; l$

2. Write the following in litres:

   (a) $9000 \; ml$ (c) $400 \; ml$

   (b) $1300 \; ml$ (d) $50 \; 500 \; ml$

By now you will have discovered that we often repeat the same process, working with the metric system. Everything is to do with 1000, except the connection between millimetres and centimetres (10) and the connections between centimetres and metres (100).

The following table shows common fractions of some of the units of measurement we have used so far.

	decimal	cm	m	km	kg	t	l
$\frac{1}{4}$	0.25	2.5 mm	25 cm	250 m	250 g	250 kg	250 *ml*
$\frac{1}{2}$	0.5	5 mm	50 cm	500 m	500 g	500 kg	500 *ml*
$\frac{3}{4}$	0.75	7.5 mm	75 cm	750 m	750 g	750 kg	750 *ml*
$\frac{1}{10}$	0.1	1 mm	10 cm	100 m	100 g	100 kg	100 *ml*

Examples:

(i) $\frac{1}{4}$ is 0.25 as a decimal.

$\frac{1}{4}$ of a centimetre is 2.5 millimetres.

(ii) $\frac{3}{4}$ is 0.75 as a decimal.

$\frac{3}{4}$ of a kilometre is 750 metres.

It is very useful to know what $\frac{1}{10}$ of a unit is, because you can then work out any number of tenths.

Example:

$\frac{1}{10}$ of a litre is 100 *ml* so $\frac{7}{10}$ of a litre is 100 × 7 = 700 *ml*

Exercise 18.6: Problem solving

Length

1. In a swimming relay race the first leg is 800 metres long, the next is 400 metres and the last two are each 200 metres long. a. 1,600 B.16

   What is the total length of the race? Give your answer in (a) metres; and (b) kilometres.

2. Emilio takes part in a 50 kilometre walk. After an hour he has covered 12.8 kilometres. How far from the finish is he? 37.2 kl

3. Metal edging for flower beds is sold in 2.5 metre lengths. Adam buys eight lengths. How far will the lengths stretch when placed end to end? 20m

4. Jack bends some wire into staples. He uses 5 centimetres of wire to make one staple. How many staples can he make from a 75 centimetre length of wire? 15

5. Auntie Mabel makes fudge which she gives to her six nieces and nephews. Each gift is in an identical box tied up with 55 centimetres of ribbon. How much ribbon does she need to tie up all six boxes? 330 cm

Mass

6. Mrs James buys a 500 gram tub of butter, a 450 gram jar of marmalade and 625 grams of bacon.
   What is the total mass of the three items? Give your answer in (a) grams; and (b) kilograms. _a. 1575 / b. 15.75_

7. Sheila opens a kilogram packet of sugar and pours 160 grams of sugar into a bowl. How many grams of sugar are left in the packet? _840g_

8. A sack of potatoes has mass 25 kilograms.
   What is the mass of six sacks? _150 kg_

9. Michael shares half a kilogram of cheese equally between his four pet mice.
   How many grams of cheese will each mouse receive? _125g each_

10. The new model of the small Rapido sports car has mass 875 kilograms. Four of these cars are delivered to the local garage.
    What is the total mass of the cars? Give your answer in (a) kilograms; and (b) tonnes. _a. 3500 Kg / b. 3.5 tonnes_

Capacity

11. Peter has two watering cans. One contains 10.5 litres and the other 7 litres. How much water is there altogether in the two watering cans? _17.5l_

12. A jug has a capacity of 3 litres. It contains 1.3 litres of milk.
    How much more milk is needed to fill the jug? _1.7l_

13. Benny buys a case of lemonade. There are 12 bottles in the case and each bottle contains $2\frac{1}{2}$ litres. How many litres of lemonade does Benny buy? _30 l_

14. A bottle contains 57 millilitres of ink. Every time Rita fills her pen with ink she uses 3 millilitres. How many times can Rita fill her pen before the bottle is empty? _19 ml_

15. Paddy buys 10 cans of Fizzo, which contain 330 millilitres of drink each. How much more or less than 3 litres of Fizzo does Paddy buy? _0.3l_

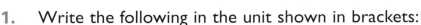

Exercise 18.7: Summary exercise ✓F

1. Write the following in the unit shown in brackets:

   (a) 4.8 cm   (mm)

   (b) 5 m   (cm)

   (c) 1.5 m   (mm)

   (d) 10.8 km   (m)

   (e) 4 g   (mg)

   (f) 3.75 kg   (g)

   (g) 0.6 t   (kg)

   (h) 6.875 *l*   (*ml*)

   (i) 40 *ml*   (*l*)

   (j) 43 000 kg   (t)

   (k) 900 g   (kg)

   (l) 13 500 mg   (g)

   (m) 800 m   (km)

   (n) 1200 mm   (m)

   (o) 50 cm   (m)

   (p) 85 mm   (cm)

   (q) 130 cm   (m)

   (r) 130 mm   (cm)

   (s) 10 g   (kg)

   (t) 10 kg   (g)

2. A mixed bag of chocolate bars contains one 450 gram bar, two 225 gram bars and four 125 gram bars.
   What is the total mass of chocolate in the bag? Give your answer in (a) grams; and (b) kilograms.

3. Victor cleared 1.23 metres in the high jump but Charlie's best effort was only 95 centimetres. How much higher than Charlie did Victor jump?

4. Six bottles of wine were drunk at a celebration. Each bottle contained 700 millilitres. How much wine was drunk? Give your answer in (a) millilitres; and (b) litres.

5. Below is a record of last week's rainfall at Boring-on-Sands, in millimetres:

Monday	Tuesday	Wednesday	Thursday	Friday	Saturday	Sunday
4	6.7	2	0	0	5	4.8

   What was the week's total rainfall? Give your answer in (a) millimetres; and (b) centimetres.

6. 50 pence coins are 2 millimetres thick. Penny makes a pile of them which is 5 centimetres high.

   (a) How many coins are there in the pile?

   (b) What is the total value of the coins?

7. The ingredients for Caribbean Cool are

       1 *l* orange juice

       $\frac{1}{2}$ *l* lemon juice

       300 *ml* grapefruit juice

       200 *ml* lime juice

       4 *l* soda water

   Ginny mixes the ingredients together.

   (a) How many litres of Caribbean Cool does she make?

   Her glasses hold a $\frac{1}{4}$ litre when full.

   (b) How many full glasses of Caribbean Cool has Ginny made?

8. Tamsin buys 750 grams of toffee. She eats half of it and then shares the remainder equally among her three brothers. What mass of toffee does each brother receive?

9. The luggage allowance on Prop Airlines is 17.5 kilograms. Teddy's suitcase has mass 21 kilograms.

   (a) How many kilograms is Teddy's case over the allowed limit?

   Teddy has to pay £5 for every 500 grams that the suitcase is over the limit.

   (b) How much does Teddy have to pay?

10. A fridge and a freezer are each 595 millimetres wide. Delia wants to place them side by side in a space which 1.195 metres wide.

    (a) Is there enough space?

    (b) How much spare space is there? **or** By how much is the space too small?

11. Old measurements of capacity include the gallon and pint. 8 pints equalled 1 gallon.

1 pint is the same as about 570 *ml*.

How many litres are roughly the equivalent of a gallon?

End of chapter activity: Traffic control

All the streets in the American town of Tooting City are straight and cross each other. A policeman has to be on duty at each crossing to control the traffic.

If there is one street, there is no crossing and no policeman is needed.

If there are two streets which cross, there is one crossing and one policeman is needed.

Here is a diagram of three streets crossing each other

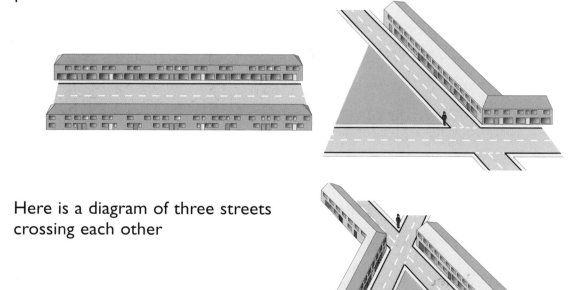

How many crossings are there and how many policemen are needed?

Now draw diagrams for four streets and then five streets. Draw the streets quite long, so you can make sure they all cross each other.

Use your diagrams to complete this table.

Streets	Policemen
1	0
2	1
3	
4	
5	

Look carefully at the table. Can you see a pattern?

Without drawing any diagrams, write down how many policeman are needed if there are six or seven streets.

Did you know?

Measurement at sea consists of an entirely different set of units.

- The depth of the sea is measured in **fathoms** which are 2 yards or 6 feet long (just under 2 metres).

- Distance across the sea is measured in **nautical/sea miles** which are about an eighth longer than a land mile.

- Speed is measured in **knots**. 1 knot = 1 nautical mile per hour, which is quicker than 1 mile per hour. (30 mph is about 35 knots).

Chapter 19: Lines

You already know how to draw and measure lines. In this chapter we are going to practise until we can draw and measure lines very accurately, to the nearest millimetre.

This ruler is marked in centimetres (cm) and millimetres (mm).

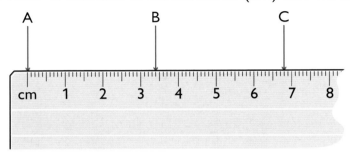

You know that 10 millimetres = 1 centimetre
and 1 millimetre = 0.1 centimetre

So the distance **AB** = 3.4 cm
and the distance **AC** = 6.8 cm

Exercise 19.1: Measuring lines

Measure the length of these lines to the nearest 0.1 centimetre (millimetre):

1. Y _____ Z

2. P _____ Q

3. M _____ N

4. O _____ P

5. Q _____ R

6. W _____ X

7.   A _____ B

8.   C _____ D

9.   S _____ T

10   E _____ F

Exercise 19.2: Drawing lines

Draw these lines accurately:

1. AB = 8.3 cm
2. PQ = 5.8 cm
3. YZ = 9.4 cm
4. WX = 10.6 cm
5. CD = 4.9 cm

6. ST = 7.1 cm
7. DE = 6.5 cm
8. MN = 11.0 cm
9. FG = 3.7 cm
10. JK = 12.2 cm

End of chapter activity: More lines

In this chapter you have measured and drawn lines which represent the distance between two points. There are many other kinds of 'lines'. See what you can find out about the following:

- Lines of latitude and longitude
- The Line (equator)
- Plimsoll line
- District and Circle line
- Production line
- Hard lines
- Silver lining

- Toe the line

- Three-line whip

- Hot line

What other 'lines' can you think of? Make a list of them.

Did you know?

A leap year happens because it takes a little more than 365 days (the length of a normal year) for the earth to go round the sun. A leap year has one extra day: February has 29 days rather than the usual 28

Every year that is divisible by 4 is a leap year (for example, 2012 and 2016 will be leap years). The exception to this rule is at the turn of a century when the year must be divisible by 400

2000 was a leap year, but the next won't be until 2400!

Chapter 20: Position – co-ordinates

You already know how to name squares on a grid by labelling the squares with letters along the bottom of the grid and numbers up the side. Here is a reminder:

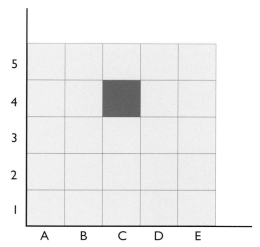

In the grid above, the shaded square is at position C4

We use a similar system to name **points**.

The grid

- There are two lines called **axes**:
  - The **horizontal** axis is called the **x axis**
  - The **vertical** axis is called the **y axis**

- The axes meet at the **origin**.

- The lines on both the axes are numbered at regular intervals, starting with 0 at the origin.

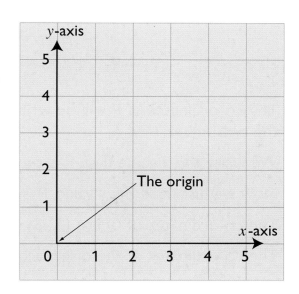

Co-ordinates

Co-ordinates (sometimes known as **ordered pairs**) can be used to give the position of any point on the grid.

Co-ordinates are written:

- in brackets; and

- with the *x* value first.

A comma separates the *x* value from the *y* value.

Example:

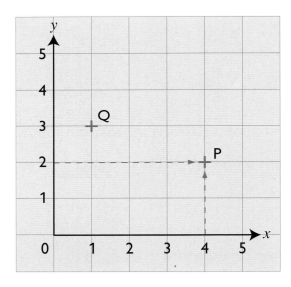

The co-ordinates of P will be written in brackets with a comma separating the two values: (,)

We write the *x* value first. P is on the line labelled 4 on the *x* axis: (4,)

Now we just need the *y* value. P is on the line labelled 2 on the *y* axis: (4, 2)

The co-ordinates of Q are (1, 3).

The co-ordinates of the origin are (0, 0).

Exercise 20.1: Reading co-ordinates (1)

Write down the co-ordinates of the points **A** to **J**.

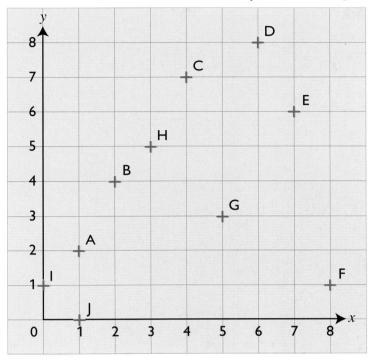

Always look carefully at the scale: sometimes only the even numbers are put in.

Example:

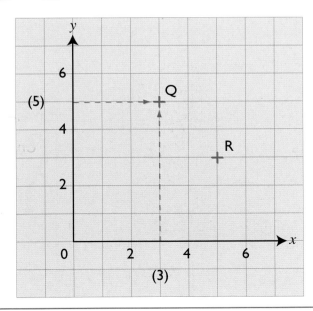

Q = (3, 5)

R = (5, 3)

Exercise 20.2: Reading co-ordinates (2)

Write down the co-ordinates of the points **A** to **J**.

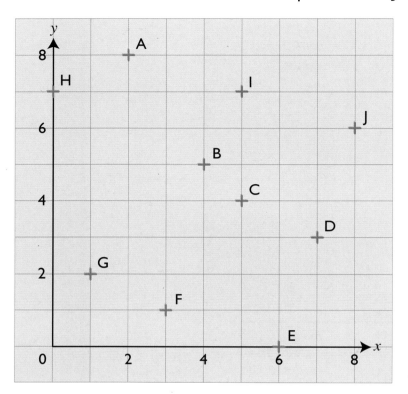

Plotting points

When plotting points on a grid, remember that **the x value comes first**.

Example:

Plot and label the point **Z** = (4, 5)

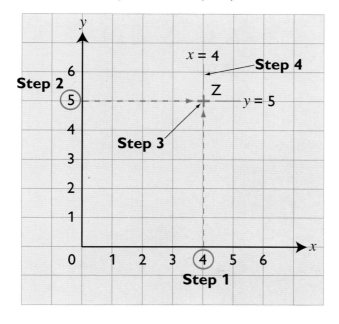

Step 1: Find the value of the x co-ordinate (4) on the x axis.

Remember: The **x** co-ordinate is the **first** co-ordinate.

The **x** axis is the **horizontal** axis.

Step 2: Find the value of the y co-ordinate (5) on the y axis.

Remember: The **y** co-ordinate is the **second** co-ordinate.

The **y** axis is the **vertical** axis.

Step 3: Mark with a cross the point where the lines x = 4 and y = 5 meet.

Step 4: Label the point Z.

Exercise 20.3: Plotting points

1. Copy the grid, then plot and name these points:

   A = (5, 2)   F = (7, 8)

   B = (8, 6)   G = (0, 2)

   C = (4, 7)   H = (2, 3)

   D = (1, 4)   I = (6, 5)

   E = (3, 1)   J = (7, 0)

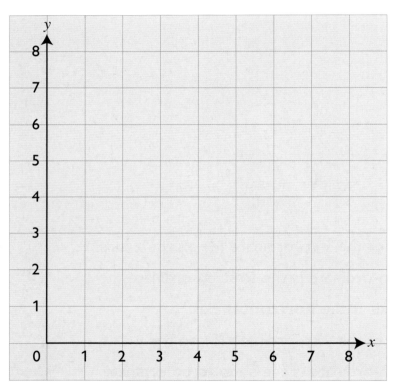

2. Copy the grid, then plot and name these points:

    A = (2, 4)   F = (2, 0)

    B = (4, 7)   G = (7, 8)

    C = (7, 2)   H = (0, 6)

    D = (5, 1)   I = (8, 3)

    E = (1, 5)   J = (6, 5)

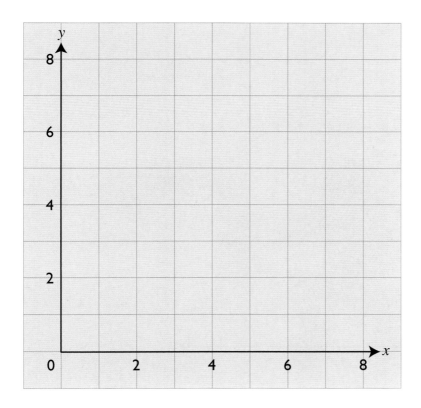

Drawing shapes

We can use co-ordinates to draw shapes: we plot the corner points and join them in order.

Example:

Plot these points and join them in order:

(2, 1), (2, 6), (5, 4), (8, 6), (8, 1), (5, 2), (2, 1)

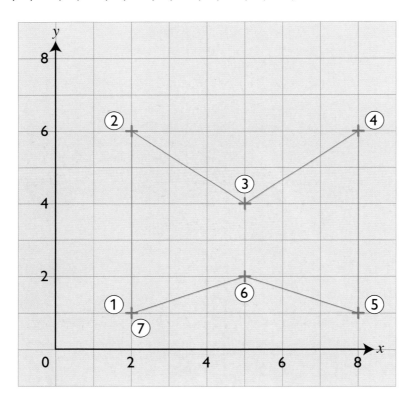

Tip: You might find it easier to join the points as you plot them.

Exercise 20.4: Drawing shapes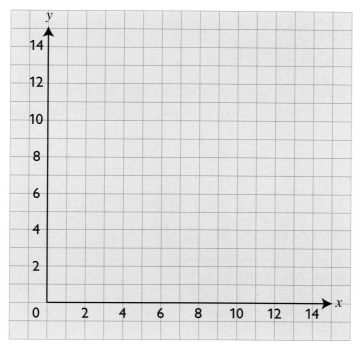

For each question, plot the points and join them in order. You will need two copies of the grid below (one for Q1–4 and one for Q5–6).

1. (1, 8), (1, 14), (4, 14), (4, 12), (1, 12)

2. (4, 1), (3, 3), (1, 4), (3, 5), (4, 7), (5, 5), (7, 4), (5, 3), (4, 1)

3. (11, 3), (10, 5), (12, 5), (11, 3), (13, 4), (13, 2), (11, 3), (12, 1), (10, 1), (11, 3), (9, 2), (9, 4), (11, 3)

4. (a) (9, 10), (9, 14), (11, 13), (9, 12)

   (b) (9, 10), (13, 10), (12, 8), (11,10)

   (c) (9, 10), (9, 6), (7, 7), (9, 8)

   (d) (9, 10), (5, 10), (6, 12), (7, 10)

5. (a) (7, 10), (4, 5), (1, 10), (4, 12), (7, 10), (1, 10)

   (b) (2, 9), (3, 9)

   (c) (5, 9), (6, 9)

   (d) (3, 4), (3, 7), (5, 7), (5, 4)

6. (a) (7, 2), (14, 2), (13, 1), (9, 1), (7, 2)

    (b) (10, 9), (10, 2)

    (c) (8, 3), (10, 8), (13, 3), (8, 3)

Drawing shapes with letters

We often label points with letters of the alphabet. When we draw shapes, we join the points in alphabetical order. Don't forget to join the last letter to the first.

Example:

Draw ABCD when A = (2, 2), B = (5, 2), C = (5, 5) and D = (2, 5).

Plot the points and join them in order: A   B   C   D   A

Tip: Write down the letter as you plot it.

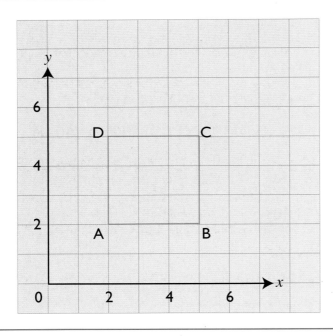

Exercise 20.5:
Drawing shapes with letters

You will need one copy of the grid below for this exercise.

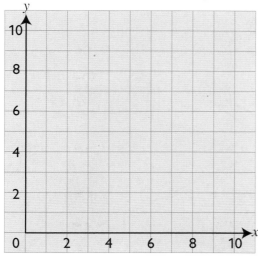

1. Draw ABC when A = (1, 7), B = (5, 7) and C = (6, 10).

2. Draw PQRS when P = (1, 2), Q = (5, 2), R = (5, 5) and S = (1, 5).

3. WXYZ when W = (8, 5), X = (10, 4), Y = (8, 9) and Z = (6, 4).

4. What special name is there for each of the three shapes you have drawn?

End of chapter activity: Making squares

You will need another copy of the grid you used for Exercise 20.5.

First you need to make the pieces of the puzzle:

● Draw ABCD when A = (2, 1), B = (5, 2), C = (4, 5) and D = (1, 4).

● Draw PQRST when P = (1, 6), Q = (3, 6), R = (6, 7), S = (6, 9) and T = (1, 9).

● Cut out the shapes ABCD and PQRST.

● On the remaining centimetre squared paper, draw shape PQRST three more times and cut them out.

Your task is to arrange all five pieces in the shape of a square.

Did you know?

The origin of running the marathon dates back to 490 BC when Pheidippides ran from Marathon to Athens to announce that the Persians had been defeated by the Greeks. History has it that he ran the distance non-stop, shouted, 'Victory is ours', then collapsed and died. The distance from Marathon to Athens is 26 miles and 385 yards (42.195 km) and is used for every marathon race. Pheidippides was the inspiration for the first staging of the race at the Athens Olympic Games in 1896.

Chapter 21: Angles and direction

In Junior Maths Book 1, Chapter 19, we learnt about an angle of 90° and how we can tell whether an angle is more or less than 90°

Example:

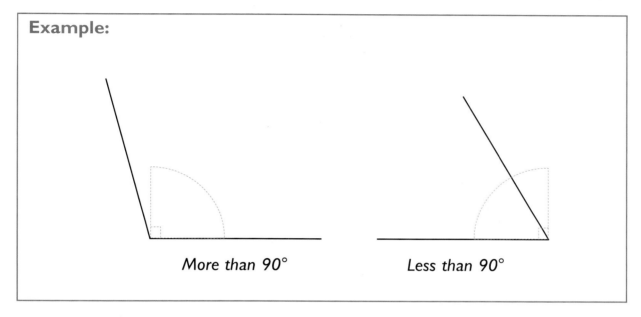

More than 90°   *Less than 90°*

In this chapter we are going to learn all about angles of less than 180°. We will identify what type an angle is, and learn how to use a protractor.

Types of angle

There are three types of angle less than 180°

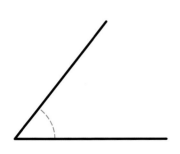

Acute angles: less than 90°

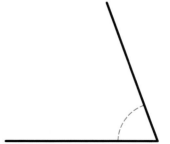

Right angles: 90°

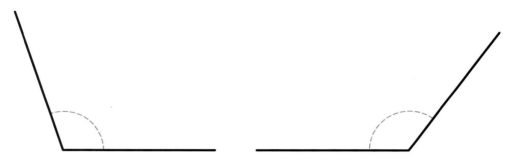

Obtuse angles: more than 90° and less than 180°

Notice that a right angle is marked differently from acute and obtuse angles.

Tip: When deciding whether an angle is acute, right or obtuse, it can help to move the page around until one of the lines is horizontal.

Exercise 21.1: Types of angle

Write down whether the figure is an acute, right or obtuse angle.

1.

6.

2.
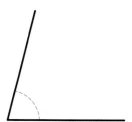

7.

3.

8.

4.
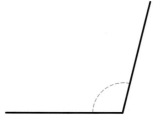

9.
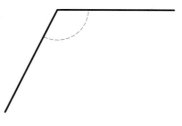

5.
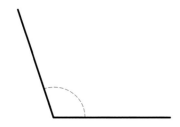

10.
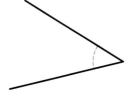

11.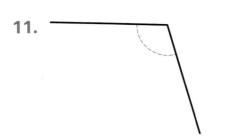

12.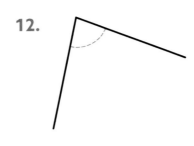

The protractor

This instrument is used to measure angles.

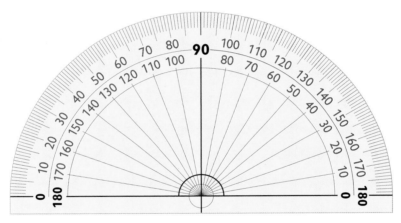

Notice that there are two scales, each measuring from 0° to 180°:

● The **outside** scale measures **clockwise** and reads **from left to right**.

● The **inside** scale measures **anticlockwise** and reads **from right to left**.

Measuring angles

Before you measure the size of an angle with your protractor, make sure you know whether your answer will be more or less than 90°

To do this, put your pencil along the bottom line of the angle and rotate it until you reach the slant line.

Ask yourself whether you have passed 90° or not.

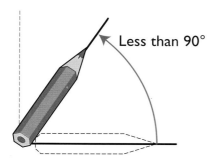

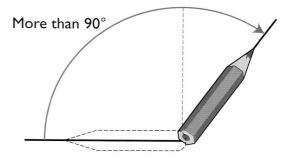

Now that you have an idea what size the angle is, you can measure it using your protractor.

- Place the + in the middle of the small semicircle on the angle. Make sure that the horizontal line at the bottom of the protractor is over the bottom line of the angle.

- Find where the other line of the angle crosses the protractor scale and read off the number. Make sure you use the correct scale.

Examples:

(i)

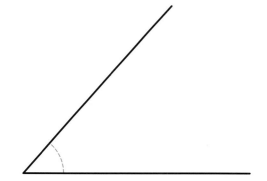

Step 1: First decide whether this angle is more or less than 90° (less).

Step 2: Now put the protractor on the angle. Line up the + and the horizontal line.

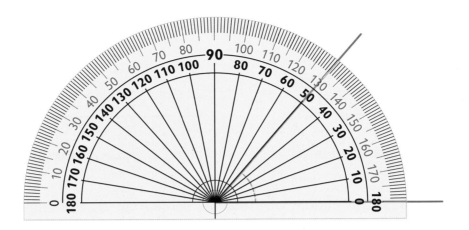

Step 3: Use the scale that starts with 0° on the side which covers the bottom line. For this angle, you want the inside scale.

Carefully read off the size of the angle: 50°

This is less than 90°, as expected.

(ii)

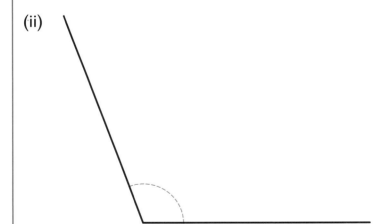

Step 1: This angle is more than 90°

Step 2: Line up the protractor.

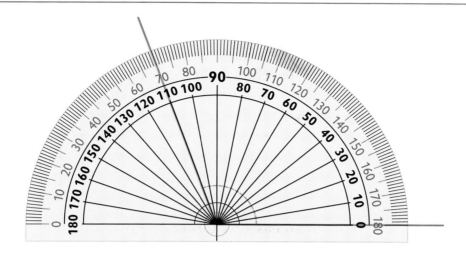

Step 3: Again, you want the inside scale.

The angle is 110°

This is more than 90°, as expected.

(iii)

Step 1: This angle is less than 90°

Step 2: Line up the protractor.

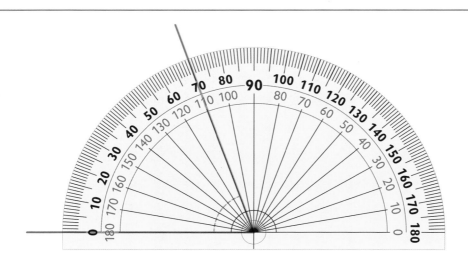

Step 3: This time you want the outside scale.

The angle is 70°

This is less than 90°, as expected.

(iv)

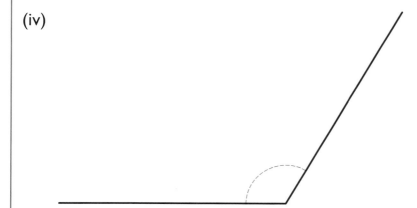

Step 1: This angle is more than 90°

Step 2: Line up the protractor.

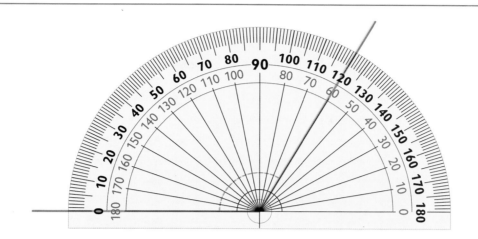

Step 3: Again, you want the outside scale.

The angle is 120°

This is more than 90°, as expected.

We used the inside scale for (i) and (ii) and the outside scale for (iii) and (iv). Can you see what each pair of angles has in common?

· ·

Exercise 21.2: Measuring angles (1)

Measure and write down the size of these angles (all the answers are multiples of 10°):

1.

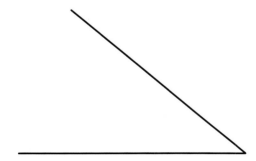

2.

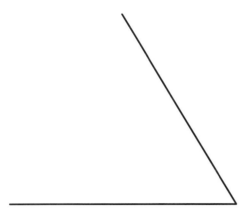

3.

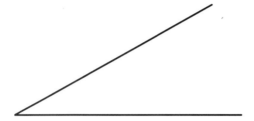

4.

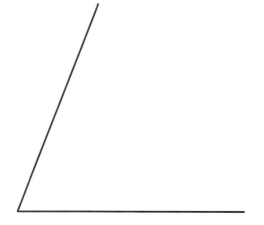

5.

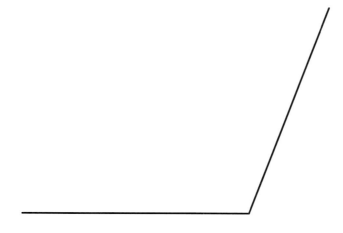

6.

7.

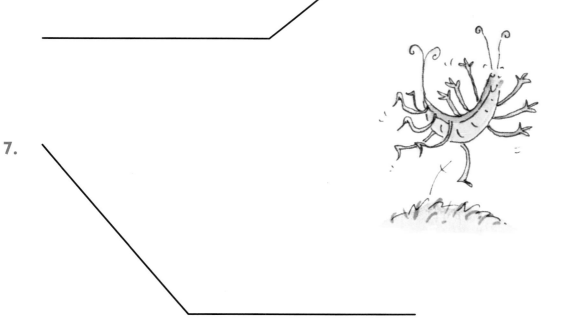

8.

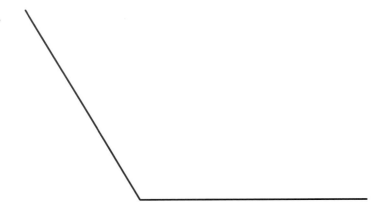

9.

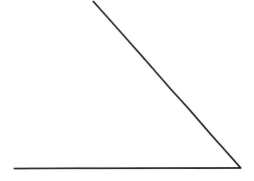

10.

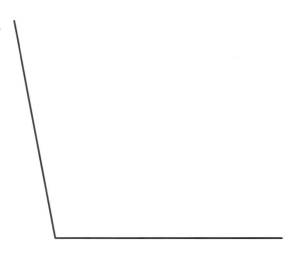

11.

12.

Before you do the next exercise, make sure you understand how important it is to read the right scale and be careful that you move along the scale in the right direction.

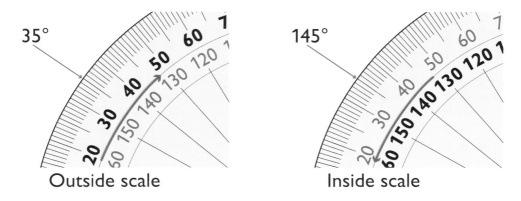

Outside scale   Inside scale

Do you understand why the mid points are 35° and 145°?

Exercise 21.3: Measuring angles (2)

Measure and write down the size of these angles (all the answers are multiples of 5°):

1.

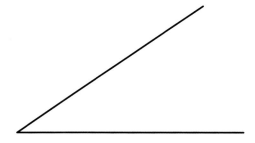

2.

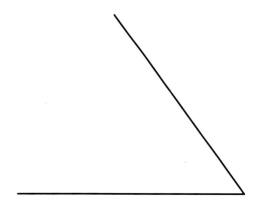

3.

4.

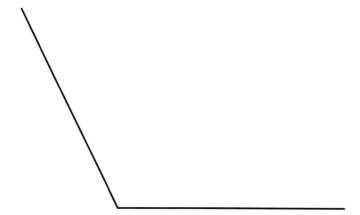

5.

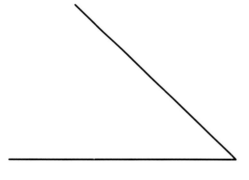

6.

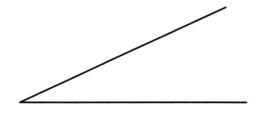

7.

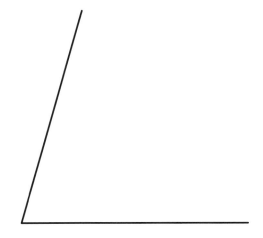

8.

9.

10.

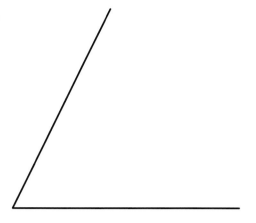

11.

12.

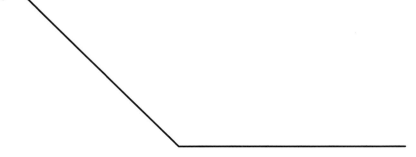

Drawing angles

By now you should be getting a feel for the size of different angles. This will help you when you draw an angle, as it is always a good idea to estimate it first.

Example:

Draw a line about 6 centimetres long and label it AB. Draw angle A = 40°

Step 1: Draw a line about 6 centimetres long and label it AB.

A   B

Step 2: Put your pencil along the line and rotate it until you think you have reached 40°. 40 is about half of 90, so the angle will be about half the size of a right angle.

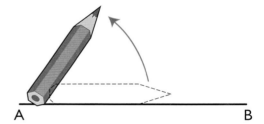

A   B

Step 3: Line up the protractor. Place the horizontal line at the bottom of the protractor over the line AB, with the + at one end.

Decide which scale you need to use: think about how you moved your pencil and use the set of figures that start with 0°. For this angle, you want the inside scale.

Find 40° on the inside scale and make a dot at the edge of the protractor.

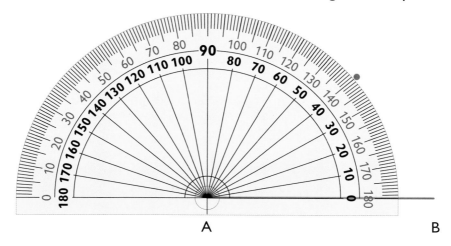

Step 4: Draw a line from A through the dot.

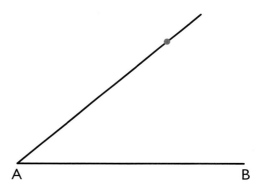

Exercise 21.4: Drawing angles

For each question draw a line about 6 centimetres long and letter it AB.

Draw the following angles:

1. angle A = 30°
2. angle A = 110°
3. angle B = 70°
4. angle B = 140°
5. angle A = 40°

6. angle B = 50°
7. angle B = 150°
8. angle A = 120°
9. angle B = 60°
10. angle A = 80°°

11. angle B = 35°

12. angle B = 115°

13. angle A = 65°

14. angle A = 125°

15. angle B = 45°

16. angle A = 135°

17. angle A = 55°

18. angle B = 75°

19. angle B = 95°

20. angle A = 105°

Angles and the hands of a clock

The hour hand of a clock turns through 360° in 12 hours;

$$360° \div 12 = 30° \text{ in 1 hour.}$$

Examples:

(i) How many degrees does the hour hand move through in 5 hours?

30 x 5 = 150°

(ii) What is the angle between the hands of the clock?

There are 4 hours between the hands.

30 x 4 = 120°

Exercise 21.5: Angles and the hands of a clock

1. Write down the number of degrees an hour hand moves through in:

   (a) 2 hours

   (b) 3 hours

   (c) 7 hours

   (d) 10 hours

   (e) half an hour

2. Write down the size of the angle between the hands of these clocks:

   (a)

   (d)

   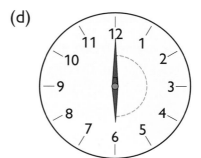

   (b)

   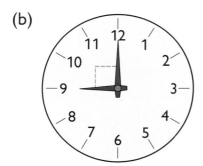

   (e)

   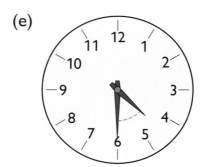

   (c)

   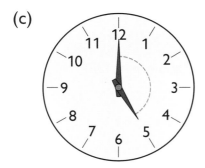

Direction – the compass

You already know the cardinal points of the compass: north, east, south and west.

There are four more commonly used points. These are halfway between the points you know already.

They are: **north-east** (NE), **south-east** (SE), **south-west** (SW), and **north-west** (NW).

They halve the right angle between the cardinal points into two lots of 45°.

If you turned clockwise from an easterly direction to a south-easterly direction, you would turn through 45°.

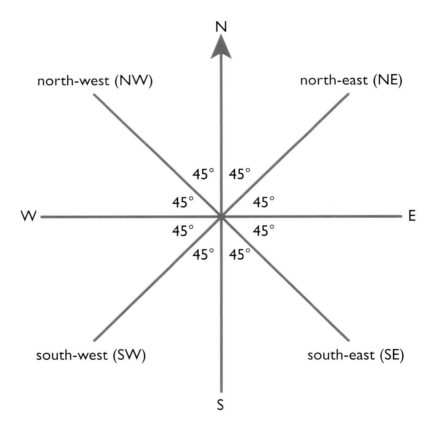

Exercise 21.6: Direction – the compass

1. Through how many degrees do you turn if you turn clockwise:

    (a) from north to north-east

    (b) from north to south-east

    (c) from north to south-west

    (d) from north to north-west

    (e) from east to south-west

    (f) from east to north-west

    (g) from south to south-west

    (h) from west to north-east

    (i) from north-east to south-east

    (j) from south-west to north-west

    (k) from north-west to north-east

    (l) from south-east to south-west

    (m) from north-east to south-west

    (n) from south-east to north-west

    (o) from south-east to north-east

2. Look carefully at the grid on the next page.

    For each question, start at P(8, 8) and move as instructed.

    Then write down the co-ordinates of the point you finish at

---

Examples:

(i) 3 squares east
    3 squares east from (8, 8) is (11, 8)

(ii) 2 squares north-west
    2 squares north-west is (6, 10)

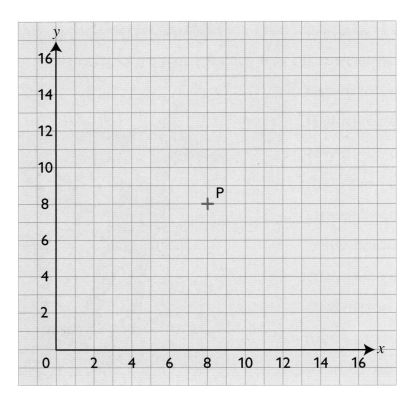

(a) 4 squares north

(b) 1 square west

(c) 5 squares east

(d) 6 squares south

(e) 3 squares south-west

(f) 5 squares north-east

(g) 6 squares south-east

(h) 2 squares north-west

(i) 3 squares west followed by 4 squares north-east

(j) 4 squares south followed by 3 squares south-west

(k) 6 squares east followed by 7 squares north-west

(l) 7 squares north followed by 5 squares south-east

(m) 4 squares north-east followed by 2 squares north-west

(n) 3 squares south-west followed by 4 squares south-east

(o) 5 squares north-west followed by 2 squares south-west

(p) 2 squares south-east followed by 5 squares north-east

(q) 4 squares west then 2 squares north and finally 5 squares south-east

(r) 5 squares south then 3 squares east and finally 5 squares north-west

(s) 3 squares north-east then 4 squares north-west and finally 5 squares south-west

(t) 3 squares south-west then 3 squares north-west and finally 5 squares east

3. Use the eight compass directions to describe the shortest route between the given squares.

Examples:

(i) From P to (8, 2)

6 squares south

(ii) From P to (11, 5)

3 squares south-east

(a) From P to (4, 8)

(b) From P to (8, 4)

(c) From P to (8, 14)

(d) From P to (14, 8)

(e) From P to (14, 2)

(f) From P to (4, 12)

(g) From P to (15, 15)

(h) From P to (0, 0)

(i) From P to (7, 12)

(j) From P to (9, 5)

Exercise 21.7: Summary exercise

1. Measure and write down the size of these angles:

   (a)

   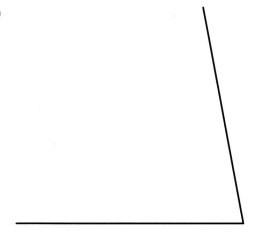

   (b)

   (c)

   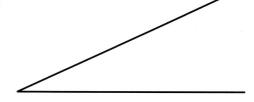

(d)

2. For each question draw a line about 6 centimetres long and letter it AB.
    Draw the following angles:
    (a) angle A = 45°   (c) angle B = 60°
    (b) angle B = 115°   (d) angle A = 95°

3. (a) Through how many degrees does the hour hand move in 1 hour?
    (b) What is the angle between the hands of a clock at 4 o'clock?

4. (a) How many degrees are there between north and north-east?
    (b) How many degrees are there in a clockwise turn from east to
         south-west?

5. (a) Write down the co-ordinates of P.

   (b) What are the co-ordinates of the point that is 3 squares west of P?

   (c) What are the co-ordinates of the point that is 4 squares south-east of P?

   (d) What is the distance and direction of Q from P?

   (e) What is the distance and direction of R from Q?

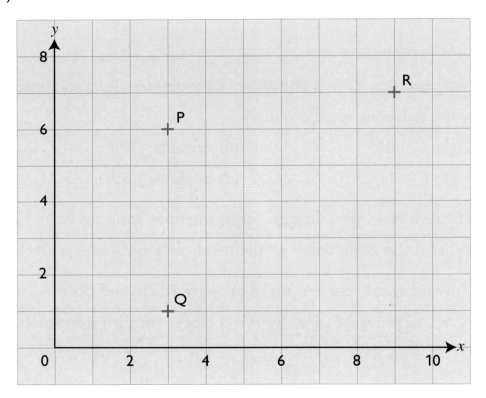

End of chapter activity: Clock shapes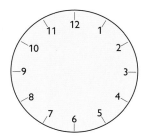

You will need at least seven
blank clock faces.

You are going to draw some shapes using the hour positions/points on the
clock face. For each shape:

●   Start at 12 and move in a clockwise direction.

●   Join the hour points with straight lines.

●   Stop when you start repeating yourself.

    Shape 1:   Join the hours in order.

                  $12 \rightarrow 1 \rightarrow 2 \rightarrow 3 \rightarrow \ldots$

    Shape 2:   Join the hours missing 1 hour each time.

                  $12 \rightarrow 2 \rightarrow 4 \rightarrow 6 \rightarrow \ldots$

    Shape 3:   Join the hours missing 2 hours each time.

                  $12 \rightarrow 3 \rightarrow 6 \rightarrow \ldots$

    Shape 4:   Join the hours missing 3 hours each time.

                  $12 \rightarrow 4 \rightarrow \ldots$

    Shape 5:   Join the hours missing 4 hours each time.

                  $12 \rightarrow 5 \rightarrow 10 \rightarrow 3 \rightarrow \ldots$

    Shape 6:   Join the hours missing 5 hours each time.

                  $12 \rightarrow 6 \rightarrow \ldots$

    Shape 7:   Join the hours missing 6 hours each time.

                  $12 \rightarrow 7 \rightarrow 2 \rightarrow 9 \rightarrow \ldots$

What do you notice? What will the next patterns be?

Did you know?

The Second Severn Crossing which joins England and Wales across the River Severn is the longest bridge in the United Kingdom. It is nearly $3\frac{1}{4}$ miles (5.128 km) long.

Chapter 22: 2D shapes

You already know that a **2-dimensional (2D) shape** can be drawn on paper. It is also called a **plane figure**.

In this chapter we are going to have a look at a number of 2D shapes: some you will have met before, while others will be new. You need to be able to recognise, describe and draw all of them. You will find it useful to have examples of the shapes around the classroom.

Circles and semicircles

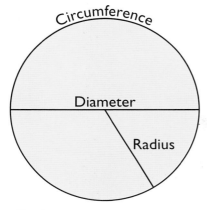

Circle

- The perimeter is called the **circumference**.

- The **radius** is the distance from the centre.

- The **diameter** divides the circle into two semicircles.

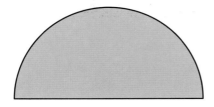

Semicircle

Triangles

A **triangle** has **three sides** and **three angles**. You need to be able to recognise three different kinds of triangle:

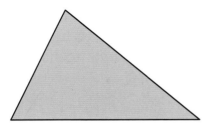

Scalene triangle

- All sides are different lengths.
- All angles are different sizes.

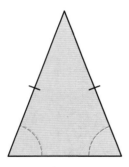

Isosceles triangle

- One pair of equal sides.
- One pair of equal angles.

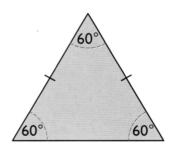

Equilateral triangle

- All sides are equal.
- All angles are 60°

Quadrilaterals

A **quadrilateral** has **four sides** and **four angles**.

Remember: Lines are **parallel** when they are the same distance apart. We show parallel lines with arrowheads.

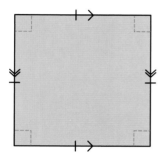

Square

- All sides are equal.
- Opposite sides are parallel.
- All angles are 90°

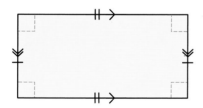

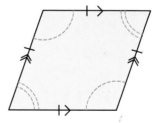

Rectangle

- Opposite sides are equal and parallel.
- All angles are 90°

Rhombus

- All sides are equal.
- Opposite sides are parallel.
- Opposite angles are equal.

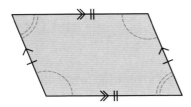

Parallelogram

- Opposite sides are equal and parallel.
- Opposite angles are equal.

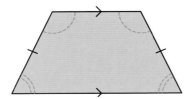

Isosceles trapezium

- One pair of parallel sides.
- Non-parallel sides are equal.
- Angles on parallels are equal.

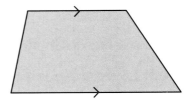

Trapezium

- One pair of parallel sides.

Kite

- Two pairs of adjacent sides are equal.
- One pair of opposite angles are equal.

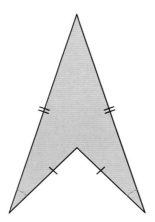

Arrowhead

- Two pairs of adjacent sides are equal.
- One pair of angles are equal.

Polygons

A **polygon** has the same number of sides as angles.

- A **pentagon** has **5** sides and angles.
- A **hexagon** has **6** sides and angles.
- A **heptagon** has **7** sides and angles.
- A **octagon** has **8** sides and angles.
- A **nonagon** has **9** sides and angles.
- A **decagon** has **10** sides and angles.

Regular figures

A figure is **regular** if all sides are equal and all angles are equal.

- An equilateral triangle is a regular triangle.
- A square is a regular quadrilateral.
- A pentagon is **any** 5-sided figure. A **regular** pentagon has all sides equal and all angles equal 108°.

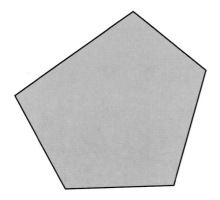

Pentagon

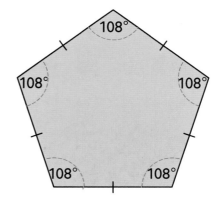

Regular pentagon

Diagonals

Diagonals are lines that join two non-adjacent **vertices** ('non-adjacent' means 'not next to each other').

Remember: A **vertex** is a corner. The plural is **vertices**.

A kite has two diagonals.

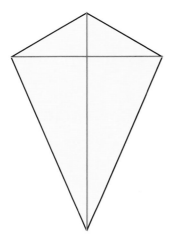

In this pentagon, we can draw two diagonals from one vertex.

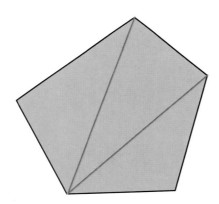

Exercise 22.1: 2D shapes

1. Name these shapes:

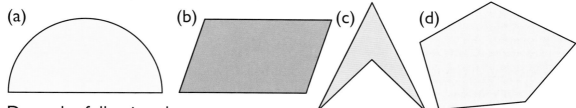

   (a)   (b)   (c)   (d)

2. Draw the following shapes:

   (a) A parallelogram   (c) An isosceles trapezium

   (b) A rhombus   (d) A hexagon

3. (a) I am a quadrilateral with all my sides equal and all angles are 90°. What am I?

   (b) I am a three-sided shape with a pair of equal sides. What am I?

   (c) The only thing that matters about me is that only one pair of my opposite four sides is equal. What am I?

   (d) I am another three-sided shape but I have nothing the same about me. What am I?

4. What is the distance from the centre of a circle to its circumference called?

5. What kind of triangle would have sides that are all 5 cm long?

6. When is a shape a **regular** shape?

7. How many sides does a decagon have?

8. What name is given to an 8-sided shape?

9. What does **parallel** mean?

10. Draw these shapes and use your diagrams to help you answer the questions.

    Square   Rectangle   Rhombus   Parallelogram   Kite

    (a) Each figure has the same number of diagonals. How many does each have?

(b) Which shapes have diagonals that are equal in length?

(c) In which shapes do the diagonals meet at 90°?

(d) In which shapes do the diagonals bisect (halve) each other?

The next exercise combines what you have learnt about 2D shapes with what you have learnt about co-ordinates. If you need to refresh your memory about plotting points, have another look at Chapter 20.

Exercise 22.2: Shapes on a grid

You will need one copy of the grid from the worksheets for this exercise.

1. (a) Draw triangle ABC when A = (1, 8), B = (1, 12) and C = (6, 10).

   (b) What kind of triangle is ABC?

2. (a) Draw triangle XYZ when X = (8, 9), Y = (8, 12) and Z = (12, 9).

   (b) What kind of triangle is XYZ?

   (c) What kind of angle is at Z?

   (d) Measure and write down the length of YZ.

3. (a) Draw PQRS when P = (1, 6), Q = (3, 8), R = (5, 6) and S = (3, 1).

   (b) What kind of quadrilateral is PQRS?

   (c) Draw in the diagonals.

   (d) Write down the size of the angle where the diagonals meet.

4. (a) Plot the points D = (8, 7), E = (6, 2) and F = (9, 2).

   (b) Join D to E to F.

   (c) Plot the point G to make DEFG a parallelogram.

   (d) Write down the co-ordinates of G.

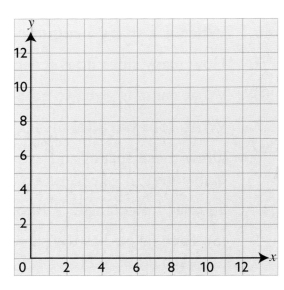

End of chapter activity: Diagonals

Follow these instructions to explore the number of **diagonals** in different 2D shapes.

- Draw five circles, each with a radius of about 3 centimetres.

- Put three dots on the circumference of the first circle, four on the second, five on the third, and so on …

- Join the dots to form a triangle, quadrilateral, pentagon and so on …

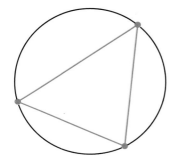 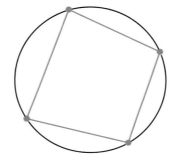 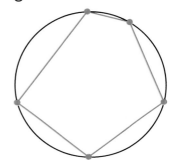

- Choose a vertex and draw as many diagonals as you can from it.

- Copy and complete the table.

Shape	Sides	Number of vertices	Number of diagonals
Triangle	3		
Quadrilateral	4		
Pentagon	5		

- Look at the table. Can you see a pattern?

  How many diagonals can be drawn from one vertex of: (a) an octagon? and (b) a decagon?

  What about a 50-sided figure?

If you want to go one stage further, try to find the **total** number of diagonals that can be drawn.

● Go round each shape and draw in as many diagonals as you can from each vertex.

● As you go round you will find some diagonals have already been drawn – don't count them again!

Here is what the pentagon will look like:

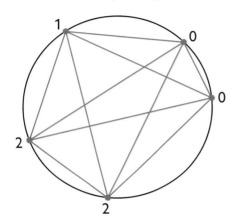

What is the total number of diagonals that can be drawn in an octagon? a decagon?

Did you know?

Don't be fooled by a name!

An **Imperial ton** is pronounced the same as a **metric tonne** but is heavier by 77 pounds (35 kilograms).

A **UK** gallon = 4.5 litres but a **US** gallon = 3.8 litres.

Chapter 23: Symmetry and reflection

A **line of symmetry** is a line along which a shape can be folded so that one half of the shape maps exactly onto the other half.

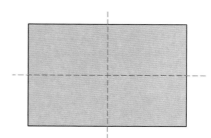

A kite has one line of symmetry   *A rectangle has two lines of symmetry*

You should already by able to recognise a line of symmetry, and complete a symmetrical shape. In this chapter we are going to find out what a line of symmetry can tell us about the shape.

Example: Triangle ABC has one line of symmetry, XY.

The two halves of the shape are the same. This means that

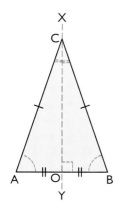

- CA = CB   so triangle ABC is isosceles (an isosceles triangle has two equal sides).

- angle A = angle B   this confirms that ABC is isosceles (an isosceles triangle also has two equal angles).

- OA = OB   XY passes through the mid point of AB. XY bisects (halves) AB.

- angle ACO = angle BCO   XY bisects angle ACB.

When shapes are exactly the same they are said to be **congruent**. In the example above, triangle AOC is congruent to triangle BOC: they are not drawn the same way round but we know that everything about them is equal; the length of the sides, the size of the angles and even their area.

Exercise 23.1: Symmetry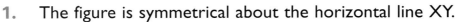

1. The figure is symmetrical about the horizontal line XY.

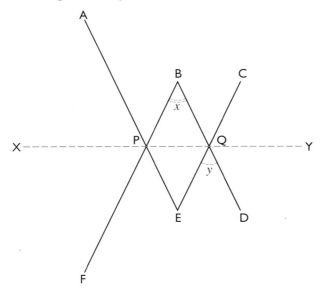

(a) Which line is equal to (i) BP; (ii) DQ?

(b) Write down any other pair of lines that are equal.

(c) Show which angles are equal to those already marked.

(d) What can you say about triangles BPQ and EPQ?

2. (a) On a copy of the grid below, draw the shape ABCDEF when
   A = (6, 0), B = (4, 1), C = (1, 7), D = (6, 3), E = (11, 7) and F = (8, 1).

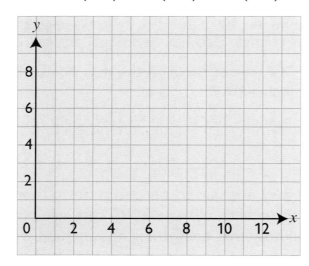

(b) What name is given to polygon ABCDEF?

(c) Draw the line of symmetry of ABCDEF.

(d) Which line is equal to (i) AF; (ii) BC?

(e) Which angle is equal to angle F?

(f) Name a triangle that is congruent to triangle ABD.

3. (a) Copy the following shapes and draw on all their lines of symmetry:

(i)   (ii)   (iii)

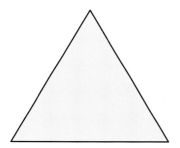  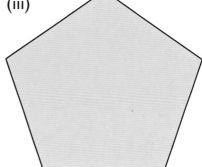

(b) Copy and complete this table.

	Name of shape	Number of sides	Number of lines of symmetry
(i)			
(ii)			
(iii)			

(c) What do you notice about the sides of each shape?

(d) Is there anything you can say to connect the number of sides and the number of lines of symmetry?

(e) What do you think the number of lines of a regular decagon will be? Give a reason for your answer.

Reflection

When you look in a mirror you see your reflection, which is an image of yourself. It is directly opposite you and your image appears to be the same distance behind the mirror as you are in front of it. Put your nose on the mirror, walk backwards and see what happens.

The mirror is a replacement for the **line of symmetry**.

In the diagrams on the next page **P** and **P′** are the image of each other after reflection in the **mirror line m**.

Notice that:

- **P** and **P′** are the same distance from the mirror line.

- The line joining them meets the mirror line at 90°.

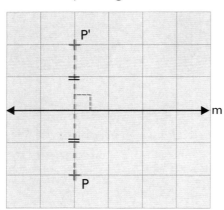 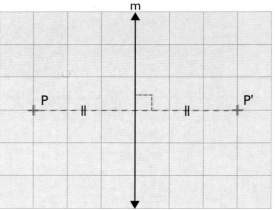

In the next diagram, △**XYZ** has been reflected in the mirror line **m** to give △**X′Y′Z′**.

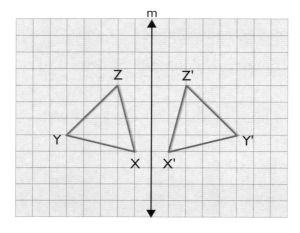

Notice that each vertex is directly opposite its image and the same distance from the mirror line.

When you reflect a shape in a mirror line, it is a good idea to reflect and label each vertex separately (if you leave the labelling until last, it is easy to put the letters in the wrong places).

Example: Reflect ABCD in the line **m** and label the image A′B′C′D′.

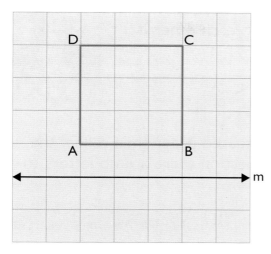

Plot each vertex in turn:

- Count the number of squares between A and the mirror line: 1

- Plot A′ 1 square away from the mirror line, opposite A.

- B is also 1 square away from the mirror line, so B′ is as well.

- C′ is 4 squares away from the mirror line (or 3 squares behind B′).

- D′ is 4 squares away from the mirror line (or 3 squares behind A′).

If you have not made any mistakes, D′ should complete the square A′B′C′D′.

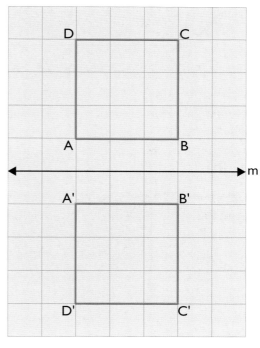

Note: The original shape and its image are always **congruent**.

The original shape and its image map onto each other if you fold along the mirror line.

. . . .

Exercise 23.2: Reflection

1. Copy the following diagrams onto squared paper, then reflect the shapes in the mirror lines. (In this question there are no letters to worry about.)

(a)

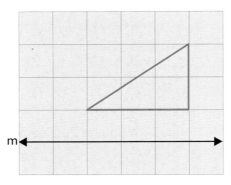

(c)

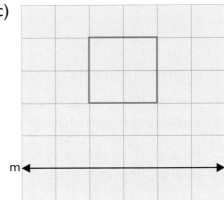

(b)

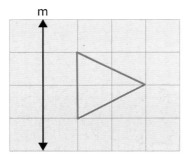

(d)

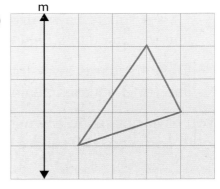

(e)

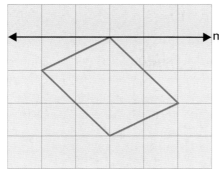

(f)

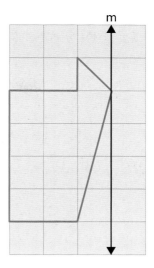

2. Copy the following diagrams onto squared paper, then reflect the shapes in the mirror lines. Label the images A'B'C', and so on.

(a)

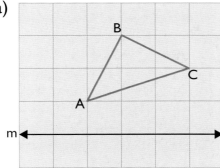

(c)

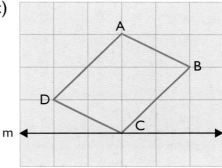

(b)

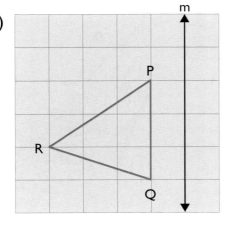

(d)

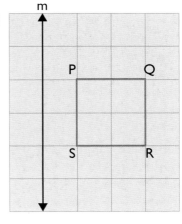

(e)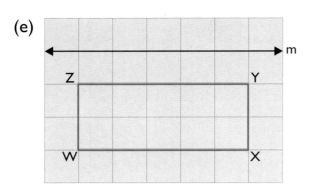

(f)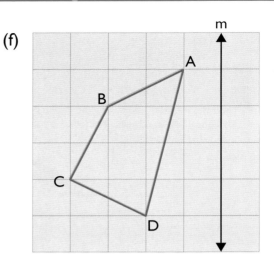

3. Copy the following diagrams onto squared paper, then reflect the shapes in the mirror lines. You might find it helps to move the page around so that the mirror line is vertical.

(a)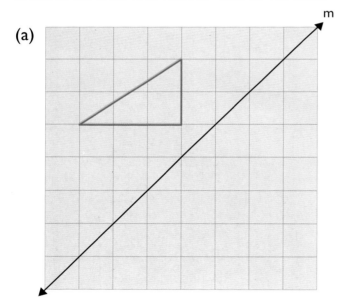

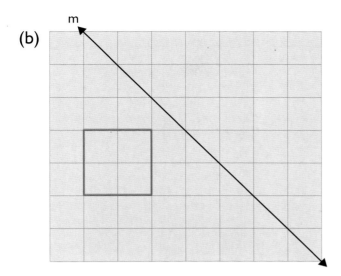

(b)

m

. . . .

End of chapter activity: Reflection by design

Think of a few examples of symmetry (reflection):

● the face of a tiger

● a butterfly with its wings spread

● the sails of a windmill or a flag.

Now make a design of your own which involves symmetry.

The line of symmetry can be repeated and there can be more than one.

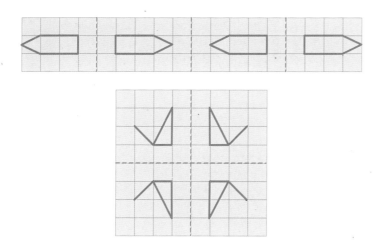

Use colour to make your design striking.

Did you know?

The emergency services sometimes use mirror writing on their vehicles so that drivers in front of them read the word correctly in their mirrors.

ƎЯIƎ

POLICE

AMBULANCE

Chapter 24: 3D shapes

You should already be familiar with the most common **three-dimensional (3D) shapes**.

Remember, each shape has:

● **faces** which are 2D (plane) shapes;

● **edges** which are straight lines where the faces meet;

● **vertices** (corners) which are points where the edges meet.

A **prism** is a solid shape that has the same cross-section along its whole length and two end faces that are identical.

Exercise 24.1: 3D shapes

1. Copy and complete the table:

	Name of shape	Shape(s) of faces	Number of faces	Number of corners	Number of edges
(i)					
(ii)					
(iii)					
(iv)					
(v)					

(i)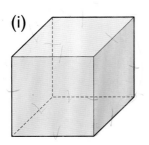

(ii)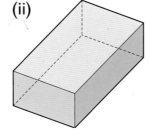

(iii)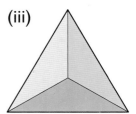

(iv)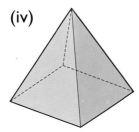

(v)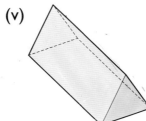

2. (a) Use your answers to Q1 to copy and complete this table.

	Number of faces (F)	Number of corners (C)	Faces and corners (F+C)	Number of edges (E)
Cube			14	12
Cuboid			10	12
Pyramid (triangle base)			8	6
Pyramid (square base)			10	8
Triangular prism			11	9

(b) Can you see a relationship between the answer in the **F+C** column and the number of **edges** (last column)?

(c) Fill in the missing numbers:

	Faces	Corners	Edges
(i)	7	10	? 15
(ii)	?	14	21
(iii)	12	? 20	30

3. This question looks at different prisms.

(i)

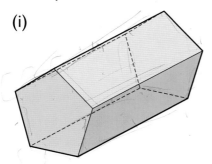

Pentagonal prism

(ii)

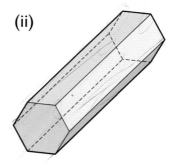

Hexagonal prism

(a) Copy and complete the table.

	Faces	Corners	Edges
(i)			
(ii)			

(b) Can you see a connection between the number of sides of the cross-section and the number of:

(i) faces;
(ii) edges?

(c) Is the sum of the 'number of faces + the number of corners' two more than the number of edges?

(d) Why do you think cube and cuboid appear in the list of prisms?

. . . .

Did you know?

$\frac{7}{10}$ (70%) of the earth's surface is covered by seas and oceans.

End of chapter activity: Monkey business

Simian, the monkey, lives in a large cage that is in the shape of a cube.

Simian is at A and his keeper places a banana at H. Simian is hungry and wants the banana but, sadly, he is not feeling very well, which means he has to use the edges of the cage and can only climb down and not up. Also, to save energy, he cannot use any edge more than once.

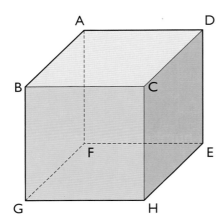

List **all** the routes Simian can take. The first is done for you.

A → B → C → D → E → H

A

If Simian lives in a **10 metre cube**, how long are the shortest and longest routes?

Chapter 25: Perimeter and area

In this chapter we are going to use what we already know about 2D shapes and measurement to explore **perimeter** and **area**.

Perimeter

Perimeter means the total distance round the outside of a shape.

Example: What is the length of the perimeter of this rectangle?

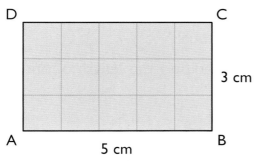

You know that the opposite sides of a rectangle are equal:

  both AB and CD = 5 cm

  both BC and DA = 3 cm

Method 1: Move around the rectangle (A → B → C → D → A), adding the lengths as you go:

  5 + 3 + 5 + 3 = 16 cm

Method 2: Add 2 lengths and 2 widths together:

  (2 x 5) + (2 x 3) = 10 + 6

  $\qquad\qquad\quad$ = 16 cm

Method 3: Find the length halfway round (1 length + 1 width) and then multiply by 2

  5 + 3 = 8

  2 x 8 = 16 cm

You should use the method you are most comfortable with.

Another word for **width** is **breadth**.

Example: What is the length of the perimeter of this square?

3 cm

You know that all sides of a square are equal.

To calculate the perimeter of a square, multiply the length of one side by 4

3 x 4 = 12 cm

Exercise 25.1: Perimeter

1. Calculate the perimeter of these shapes (they are drawn on centimetre squared paper):

    (a)

    16

    (b)

    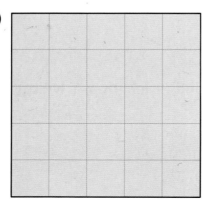

    20

(c)

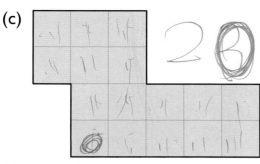

(d)

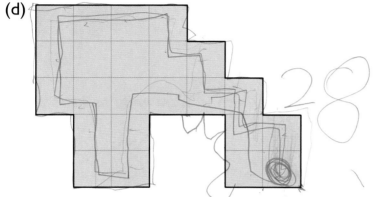

2. **What are the lengths of the perimeters of these rectangles?**

	Length	Width
(a)	8 cm	5 cm 26 cm
(b)	12 cm	13 cm 50 cm
(c)	25 cm	15 cm 80 cm
(d)	6.4 cm	4 cm 20.8 cm
(e)	10.5 cm	9.5 cm 40 cm

3. **What are the lengths of the perimeters of squares with these sides?**

(a) 9 cm 36

(b) 16 cm 64

(c) 20 cm 80

(d) 4.5 cm 18

(e) 7.2 cm 28.8

(f) 6.6 cm 26.2

If you know the perimeter and the length of a rectangle, you can find the width of the rectangle. If you know the perimeter and the width, you can find the length.

Remember: length + width = $\frac{1}{2}$ the perimeter

Examples:

(i) What is the width of a rectangle which is 6 cm long and has a perimeter of 16 cm?

length + width = $\frac{1}{2}$ the perimeter

6 + width = 8

width = 8 − 6

width = 2 cm

(ii) What is the length of a rectangle which is 5 cm wide and has a perimeter of 40 cm?

length + width = $\frac{1}{2}$ the perimeter

length + 5 = 20

length = 20 − 5

length = 15 cm

If you know the perimeter of a square, you can find the length of a side by dividing by 4 (because all 4 sides of a square are equal).

Example:

What is the length of a side of a square whose perimeter is 40 cm?

length = perimeter ÷ 4

length = 40 ÷ 4

length = 10 cm

Exercise 25.2: Calculating length and width

1. Copy and complete the following:

	Perimeter	Length	Width
(a)	20 cm	6 cm	4 cm
(b)	36 cm	15 cm	3 cm
(c)	60 cm	20 cm	10 cm
(d)	48 cm	16 cm	8 cm
(e)	9 cm	3 cm	1.5 cm

2. Calculate the side lengths of squares with the following perimeters:

    (a) 16 cm 4 cm

    (b) 64 cm 16 cm

    (c) 100 cm 25 cm

Area

Area means how much surface is covered by a shape.

It is measured in **square units**. The most common are

- the square centimetre (**cm²**)

- the square metre (**m²**)

Draw a square of side 1 metre on the floor in the corner of the room: it may be larger than you thought!

- A sheet of A4 paper is 600 cm².

- A classroom can be about 80 m².

- A football pitch is about 8000 m².

A square millimetre (**mm²**) is very small and a square kilometre (**km²**) is very large. We do not come across them very often in everyday life.

One way to find an area is by **counting squares**.

Examples:

Calculate the area of these shapes (they are drawn on centimetre squared paper):

(i)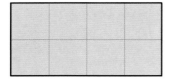

Area = 8 cm²

Did you count up each square or did you find a quicker way to work out the answer?

(ii)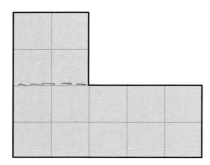

Area = 14 cm²

How did you work out the answer? Did you split it up into two shapes?

(iii)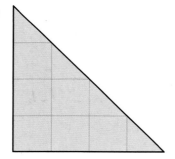

Area = 8 cm²

Did you notice that the four half squares make up two whole squares? Or did you find the answer another way?

Make sure you understand the answers to the example above, however you reached them.

Exercise 25.3: Area

Calculate the area of these shapes (they are drawn on centimetre squared paper):

1.

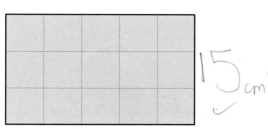

15 cm^2

2.

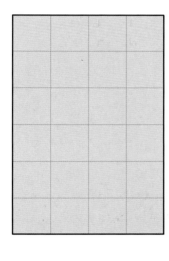

24 cm^2

3.

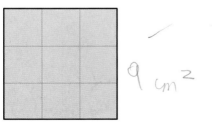

9 cm^2

4.

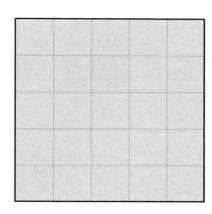

25 cm^2

5.

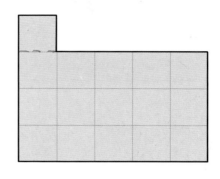

16 cm^2

6.

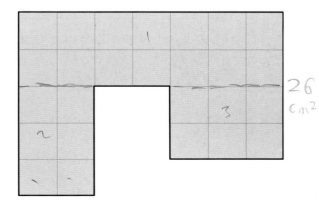

26 cm^2

7. 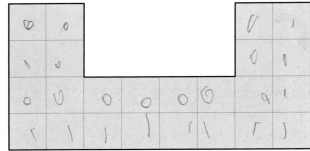 24 cm2

8. 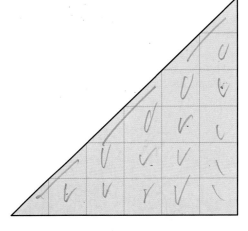 18 cm2

9. 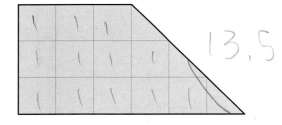 13.5 cm2

10. 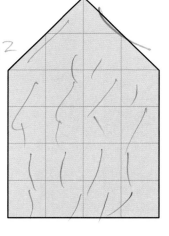 20 cm2

Fv

11.

15 cm2

12.

10 cm2

13.

8 cm2

14.

18 cm

15.

63 cm

Exercise 25.4: Summary exercise

1. What is the length of the perimeter of a rectangle that measures 9 centimetres by 5 centimetres? *28*

2. How long is the perimeter of a 7 centimetre square? *28*

3. The perimeter of a rectangle is 44 centimetres. Its shorter side is 7 centimetres.

    What is the length of the longer side? *15*

4. Calculate the width of a rectangle that is 25 centimetres long and has a perimeter of 80 centimetres. *15*

5. What is the width of a rectangle with length 12 cm and perimeter 40 cm? *8*

6. What is the length of a side of a square whose perimeter is 24 centimetres? *6*

7. Calculate the area of these shapes (they are drawn on centimetre squared paper):

    (a)

    24 cm²

    (b)

    16 cm²

(c)

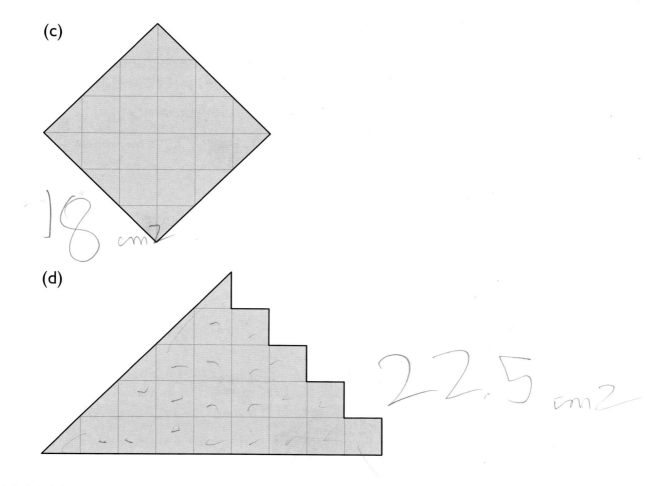

18 cm²

(d)

22.5 cm²

. . . .

End of chapter activity: Same perimeter, different area

- On centimetre squared paper, draw all the rectangles (including squares) which have a perimeter of 24 centimetres. (There are six altogether. Start with 11 cm by 1 cm.)

- Calculate the area of each rectangle and write it down inside the shape.

- What is the largest area?

- What is the name of the shape that gives the largest area?

Now comes the clever bit! By thinking about what you have just done, can you calculate the largest area that can be enclosed by a quadrilateral whose perimeter is 40 cm?

Did you know?

Over 83 square kilometres of wrapping paper ends up in rubbish bins each Christmas. That is an area larger than Guernsey in the Channel Islands. Remember to be green and recycle!

Chapter 26: Mental strategies

Teacher's introduction

If you used *Junior Maths Book 1* you will be familiar with this Chapter on Mental Strategies. We have repeated it in this book because you may find it necessary to revisit or visit for the first time the various strategies. Exercises for practice are available as downloadable worksheets from the Galore Park website www.galorepark.co.uk

The National Numeracy Strategy states that: 'In the early years children will use oral methods, in general moving from counting objects or fingers one by one to more sophisticated **mental counting strategies**. During the first few years children should be encouraged to build up a store of these strategies to enable them to manipulate and compute calculations with more ease.'

There are no right or wrong methods: not everybody will approach a mental calculation in the same way, nor need they. When a class was asked 'what is a half of 170?' the following answers were forthcoming:

Anne $\qquad (100 \div 2) + (70 \div 2)$

$\qquad\qquad = 50 + 35$

$\qquad\qquad = 85$

Ben $\qquad (\frac{1}{2}$ of $160) + (\frac{1}{2}$ of $10)$

$\qquad\qquad = 80 + 5$

$\qquad\qquad = 85$

Carol $\qquad (\frac{1}{2}$ of $180) - (\frac{1}{2}$ of $10)$

$\qquad\qquad = 90 - 5$

$\qquad\qquad = 85$

David $\qquad (200 \div 2) - (\frac{1}{2}$ of $30)$

$\qquad\qquad = 100 - 15$

$\qquad\qquad = 85$

Eve $\qquad$ I just saw the answer!

None of these methods is 'better' than the others, although one wonders whether Eve is a mathematical genius or just good at guessing! What is important is not what method pupils use but whether they can explain verbally what they have done; discussion of the various methods is particularly valuable. In the end, the 'best' method is simply the one that the child is most at ease with.

This chapter does not purport to be a comprehensive catalogue of strategies; rather it sets out to suggest a few ideas that might be worth discussing.

A child should attempt a particular strategy only when the teacher thinks that child is ready to benefit from its study.

Addition

Partition

It is often possible to partition (separate) a number into tens and units. This means that the same calculation can be tackled in many different ways.

Example: $46 + 23$

Think of 46 as $(40 + 6)$ or 23 as $(20 + 3)$

So $46 + 23 = 46 + (20 + 3)$

$= 66 + 3$

$= 69$

or $46 + 23 = (40 + 6) + 23$

$= 63 + 6$

$= 69$

or $46 + 23 = (40 + 6) + (20 + 3)$

$= 60 + 6 + 3$

$= 69$

$2 + 2 + 2$?

Or, think of 46 as (50 − 4) or 23 as (30 − 7)

So $\qquad$ 46 + 23 = 46 + (30 − 7)

$\qquad\qquad\qquad$ = 76 − 7

$\qquad\qquad\qquad$ = 69

or $\qquad$ 46 + 23 = (50 − 4) + 23

$\qquad\qquad\qquad$ = 73 − 4

$\qquad\qquad\qquad$ = 69

or $\qquad$ 46 + 23 = (50 − 4) + (30 − 7)

$\qquad\qquad\qquad$ = 80 − 4 − 7

$\qquad\qquad\qquad$ = 69

You could in fact use the different ways of thinking of 46 and 23 in **any combination**:

$\qquad\qquad$ 46 = (40 + 6) or (50 − 4)

and $\qquad$ 23 = (20 + 3) or (30 − 7)

Exercise 26.1: Using addition strategies

Use of doubles

When the numbers you are working with are close to each other, you can often use doubles.

Tip: You need to know your 2 times table for this way of thinking!

Examples:

(i)   80 + 70

Think of 80 as (70 + 10)

So   80 + 70 = (70 + 10) + 70

$\qquad\qquad\qquad\qquad$ = (70 × 2) + 10   We have 2 lots of 70 so we put them together. We can now double 70 to give 140

$\qquad\qquad\qquad\qquad$ = 140 + 10

$\qquad\qquad\qquad\qquad$ = 150

Or, think of 70 as (80 − 10)

So   80 + 70 = 80 + (80 − 10)

$\qquad\qquad\qquad\qquad$ = (80 × 2) − 10   We have 2 lots of 80 so we put them together. We can now double 80 to give 160

$\qquad\qquad\qquad\qquad$ = 160 − 10

$\qquad\qquad\qquad\qquad$ = 150

(ii)   29 + 27

Think of 29 as (30 − 1) and 27 as (30 − 3)

So   29 + 27 = (30 − 1) + (30 − 3)

$\qquad\qquad\qquad\qquad$ = (30 × 2) − 1 − 3   We have 2 lots of 30 so we put them together. We can now double 30 to give 60

$\qquad\qquad\qquad\qquad$ = 60 − 1 − 3

$\qquad\qquad\qquad\qquad$ = 56

Or, think of 29 as (28 + 1) and 27 as (28 − 1)

So   29 + 27 = (28 + 1) + (28 − 1)

$\qquad\qquad\qquad\qquad$ = (28 × 2) + 1 − 1   We have 2 lots of 28 so we put them together. We can now double 28 to give 56

$\qquad\qquad\qquad\qquad$ = 56

Exercise 26.2: Doubling

Using a number line

Another way to add two numbers is to use a number line: as you move along the line, you can make notes to help you find the answer.

Examples:

(i) **86 + 57**

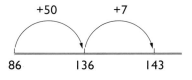

So 86 + **57** = 143

Break the number to be added down into easier steps. Here, think of 57 as 50 + 7

(ii) **273 + 588**

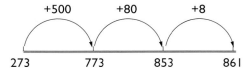

So 273 + **588** = 861

(iii) **68 + 96 + 85**

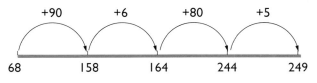

So 68 + **96** + **85** = 249

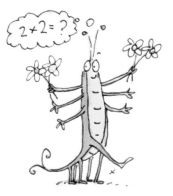

Exercise 26.3: Addition using a number line

Subtraction

Like addition, you can do subtraction in many different ways.

Counting on

When the numbers you are working with are close to each other, you can simply count on from one to the other.

Example: 93 – 88

88	89	90	91	92	93

Here you have counted on 5 to get from 88 to 93

So 93 – 88 = 5

Exercise 26.4: Subtracting by 'counting on'

Counting on using a number line

If the numbers you are working with are not close together, you can count on using a number line. As before, use notes to help you find the answer.

Examples:

(i) 93 – 46

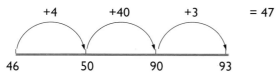

So 93 – 46 = 47

(ii) 806 – 297

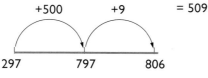

So 806 – 297 = 509

or:

So 806 – 297 = 509

Exercise 26.5:
Subtraction with a number line (1)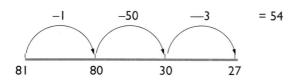
Counting back

When the numbers you are working with are close to each other, you might want to count back instead.

Examples:

(i) 23 – 17

23   22   21   20   19   18   17

Here you have counted back **6** to get from 23 to 17

So 23 – 17 = 6

(ii) 301 – 298

301   300   299   298

301 – 298 = 3

Exercise 26.6: Subtracting by 'counting back'
Counting back using a number line

Again, if the numbers are not close together, you will find a number line useful.

Examples:

(i) 81 – 27

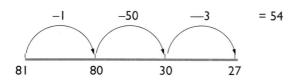

So 81 – 27 = **54**

(ii) 574 – 148

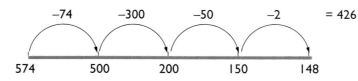

So 574 – 148 = **426**

Exercise 26.7:
Subtraction with a number line (2)

Addition and subtraction

Remember:

- It **does not** matter in what order you **add**:
  4 + 3 = 7 and 3 + 4 = 7

- It **does** matter in what order you **subtract**:
  9 − 5 is not the same as 5 − 9

Addition and **subtraction** are the **inverse** (opposite) of each other. If we look at the two processes together, we can see how they are connected.

Given that 65 + 17 = 82, it follows that 17 + 65 = 82

It also follows that **82 − 65 = 17**
and that **82 − 17 = 65**

We can use the relationship between addition and subtraction to find missing numbers.

Examples:

(i)   45 + 31 = *   * = 76   Simply add the numbers

(ii)   31 + 45 = *   * = 76   Again, add the numbers: the answer will be the same as for part (i), because the numbers are the same.

(iii)   76 − * = 45   * = 31   Subtract: 76 − 45

(iv)   76 − * = 31   * = 45   Subtract: 76 − 31

(v)   * − 31 = 45   * = 76   Add: 45 + 31

(vi)   * − 45 = 31   * = 76   Add: 31 + 45

(vii) * + 16 = 48   * = 32   Subtract: 48 − 16

(viii) 43 + * = 80   * = 37   Subtract: 80 − 43

(ix)   * − 38 = 19   * = 57   Add: 19 + 38

(x)   45 − * = 27   * = 18   Subtract: 45 − 27

Multiplication

Let's start with some helpful hints about tables which will help us in our use of mental strategies.

The ten times and five times tables

Remember:

- Numbers in the 10 times table always end in 0
  (the units digit moves 1 place left)

- Numbers in the 5 times table end in 0 or 5

Since 10 = (2 x 5) a multiple of 10 is twice the same multiple of 5

	10 times	**5 times**
(x1)	10	5
(x2)	20	10
(x3)	30	15
(x4)	40	20

To multiply by 5, multiply by 10 and **halve the answer**.

Example:	16 x 5
	$16 \times 10 = 160$ and $\frac{1}{2}$ of $160 = 80$
	So $16 \times 5 = 80$

To multiply by 20, multiply by 10 and **double the answer**.

or   **double** and multiply by 10

Example:	12 x 20
	$12 \times 10 = 120$ and $2 \times 120 = 240$
	So $12 \times 20 = 240$

or	$12 \times 2 = 24$ and $24 \times 10 = 240$
	So $12 \times 20 = 240$

Note: $12 \times 10 \times 2 = 12 \times 2 \times 10 = 240$

Multiples of one hundred and multiples of fifty

Remember:

- Multiples of 100 end in 00
- Multiples of 50 end in 00 or 50

The two times, four times and eight times tables

Let us compare the first few multiples of each of these tables:

	2 times	4 times	8 times
(×1)	2	4	8
(×2)	4	8	16
(×3)	6	12	24
(×4)	8	16	32

$4 = 2 \times 2$ so **multiples of 4** are **twice** (double) the **multiples of 2**

$8 = 2 \times 4$ so **multiples of 8** are **twice** (double) the **multiples of 4**

or **twice** the **multiples of 2 doubled!**

To multiply by 4, **double and double** again.

Example: 16 x 4

$16 \times 2 = 32$ and $32 \times 2 = 64$

So $16 \times 4 = 64$

To multiply by 8, **multiply by 4** and **double the answer**

or **double** and **multiply the answer by 4**

or **double** and **double** and **double** again.

Example:	15 x 8
	15 x 4 = 60 and 60 x 2 = 120
or	15 x 2 = 30 and 30 x 4 = 120
or	15 x 2 = 30 and 30 x 2 = 60 and 60 x 2 = 120
	So 15 x 8 = 120

Note: 15 x 4 x 2 = 15 x 2 x 4 = 15 x 2 x 2 x 2 = 120

The six times table

6 = 3 x 2

To multiply by 6, **multiply by 3** and **double**

or **multiply by 2** and **treble**.

Example:	15 x 6
	15 x 3 = 45 and 45 x 2 = 90
or	15 x 2 = 30 and 30 x 3 = 90
	So 15 x 6 = 90

Note: All **multiples of even** numbers are **even**. They end in 0, 2, 4, 6 or 8

The nine times table

9 = 3 x 3

To multiply by 9, multiply by 3 and **treble**.

There are also some other patterns to notice.

$$1 \times 9 = 9$$
$$2 \times 9 = 18$$
$$3 \times 9 = 27$$
$$4 \times 9 = 36$$
$$5 \times 9 = 45$$
$$6 \times 9 = 54$$
$$7 \times 9 = 63$$
$$8 \times 9 = 72$$
$$9 \times 9 = 81$$
$$10 \times 9 = 90$$

Pattern 1:	The **sum of the digits** of the product is **always 9** or **a multiple of 9** (1 + 8 = 9, 2 + 7 = 9 and so on).
Pattern 2:	The **tens digit of the product** of the first 10 multiples of 9 is **1 less than the number of nines** (1 x 9 = 09, 2 x 9 = 18, 3 x 9 = 27 and so on).

Multiplying by ten and by one hundred

When we **multiply by 10**, the digits move **1 place to the left**.

The **Units** digit moves to the **Tens** column.

Examples:

(i)   7 x 10 = 70

(ii)   15 x 10 = 150

(iii)   201 x 10 = 2010

When we **multiply by 100**, the digits move **2 places to the left**.

The **Units** digit moves to the **Hundreds** column.

Examples

(i)   4 x 100 = 400

(ii)   26 x 100 = 2600

Multiplication strategies

Partition

We can often break a multiplication down into stages by partitioning (separating) one or more of the numbers into a multiple of 10 and a unit.

Examples:

(i)   47 x 4 = (40 + 7) x 4   Think of 47 as (40 + 7)

                  = (40 x 4) + (7 x 4)   Multiply both the 40 and the 7 by 4

                  = 160 + 28   Add the results together.

                  = 188

(ii)   78 x 9 = (70 + 8) x 9

                  = (70 x 9) + (8 x 9)

                  = 630 + 72

                  = 702

        or   78 x 9 = 78 x (10 − 1)

                  = (78 x 10) − (78 x 1)

                  = 780 − 78

                  = 702

(iii) $83 \times 13 = 83 \times (10 + 3)$
$= (83 \times 10) + (83 \times 3)$
$= 830 + [(80 + 3) \times 3]$
$= 830 + (80 \times 3) + (3 \times 3)$
$= 830 + 240 + 9$
$= 1079$

(iv) $67 \times 18 = 67 \times (10 + 8)$
$= (67 \times 10) + (67 \times 8)$
$= 670 + [(60 + 7) \times 8]$
$= 670 + (60 \times 8) + (7 \times 8)$
$= 670 + 480 + 56$
$= 1206$

Exercise 26.8: Multiplication by partition

Use of factors

You might need to break down one or more of the numbers into its factors. Numbers that divide exactly into another number are called **factors**. For example: **3** and **6** are factors of **12**. In fact when you learn your times tables you are studying factors.

Examples:

(i) $27 \times 20 = 27 \times 10 \times 2$
$= 270 \times 2$
$= 540$

or $27 \times 20 = 27 \times 2 \times 10$
$= 54 \times 10$
$= 540$

(ii) $8 \times 27 = 8 \times 9 \times 3$
         $= 72 \times 3$
         $= 216$

Exercise 26.9: Multiplying using factors

Doubling

When doubling a number, look to see if you can break the calculation down by splitting the number.

Example: Double 79

$79 \times 2 = (70 + 9) \times 2$
$= (70 \times 2) + (9 \times 2)$
$= 140 + 18$
$= 158$

or $79 \times 2 = (80 - 1) \times 2$
$= (80 \times 2) - (1 \times 2)$
$= 160 - 2$
$= 158$

Building up tables by doubling

You can build up a times table by doubling.

Examples:

(i)   What is 16×35?

$1 \times 35 = 35$
$2 \times 35 = 70$ (35×2)
$4 \times 35 = 140$ (70×2)
$8 \times 35 = 280$ (140×2)
$16 \times 35 = 560$ (280×2)

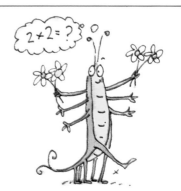

(ii) What is 35 × 23?

Think of 23 as 16 + 4 + 2 + 1

So 35 × 23 = (35 × 16) + (35 × 4) + (35 × 2) + (35 × 1)

$\qquad$ = 560 + 140 + 70 + 35

$\qquad$ = 805

Alternatively, think of 23 as 16 + 8 − 1

So 35 × 23 = (35 × 16) + (35 × 8) − (35 × 1)

$\qquad$ = 560 + 280 − 35

$\qquad$ = 805

Exercise 26.10: Multiplying using doubling

Division

Remember:

- **It does not matter in what order you multiply:**
     4 × 3 = 12
  and   3 × 4 = 12

- **It does matter in what order you divide:**
     8 ÷ 2 is not the same as 2 ÷ 8

Multiplication and **division** are the **inverse** (opposite) of each other. The connection between multiplication and division is based on tables.

Compare	A	B	C
	1 × 6 = 6	6 ÷ 6 = 1	6 ÷ 1 = 6
	2 × 6 = 12	12 ÷ 6 = 2	12 ÷ 2 = 6
	3 × 6 = 18	18 ÷ 6 = 3	18 ÷ 3 = 6
	4 × 6 = 24	24 ÷ 6 = 4	24 ÷ 4 = 6
	5 × 6 = 30	30 ÷ 6 = 5	30 ÷ 5 = 6
	6 × 6 = 36	36 ÷ 6 = 6	36 ÷ 6 = 6
	7 × 6 = 42	42 ÷ 6 = 7	42 ÷ 7 = 6 etc

In **column A** the factors are multiplied together to give the product.

In **columns B** and **C** the product is divided by one factor; the answer is the other factor.

Given that 5 x 6 = 30 it follows that   6 x 5 = 30

It also follows that: 30 ÷ 5 = 6

and that: 30 ÷ 6 = 5

We can use the relationship between multiplication and division to find missing numbers.

Examples:

(i)   9 x 8 = *   * = 72   Multiply: 9 x 8

(ii)   8 x 9 = *   * = 72   Multiply: 8 x 9 The answer will be the same as for (i), because the numbers are the same

(iii)   * x 9 = 72   * = 8   Divide: 72 ÷ 9

(iv)   * x 8 = 72   * = 9   Divide: 72 ÷ 8

(v)   72 ÷ * = 8   * = 9   Divide: 72 ÷ 8

(vi)   72 ÷ * = 9   * = 8   Divide: 72 ÷ 9

(vii) * ÷ 8 = 9   * = 72   Multiply: 8 x 9

(viii) * ÷ 9 = 8   * = 72   Multiply: 9 x 8

(ix)   * x 7 = 21   * = 3   Divide: 21 ÷ 7

(x)   * ÷ 8 = 7   * = 56   Multiply: 8 x 7

(xi)   48 ÷ * = 6   * = 8   Divide: 48 ÷ 6

(xii) 5 x * = 45   * = 9   Divide: 45 ÷ 5

Division by ten and by one hundred

When **dividing by 10**, the figures move **1 place** to the **right**: the **Tens** digit moves to the **Units** column.

> **Examples:**
>
> (i) $80 \div 10 = 8$
>
> (ii) $500 \div 10 = 50$

When **dividing by 100**, the figures move **2 places** to the **right**: the **Hundreds** digit moves to the **Units** column.

> **Examples:**
>
> (i) $300 \div 100 = 3$
>
> (ii) $2500 \div 100 = 25$

Division by five

$10 = 2 \times 5$

To **divide by 5**, **divide by 10** and **double** the answer.

> **Example:** $80 \div 5$
>
> $80 \div 10 = 8$ and $8 \times 2 = 16$
>
> So $80 \div 5 = 16$

Fractions of numbers

Questions that ask you to find '$\frac{1}{2}$ of', 'a third of', 'a quarter of' and so on are really just division sums in disguise:

- 'finding $\frac{1}{2}$ of' is the same as dividing by 2

- 'finding $\frac{1}{3}$ of' is the same as dividing by 3

- 'finding $\frac{1}{4}$ of' is the same as dividing by 4

Division by two, four and eight

When dividing by two, it sometimes helps to split the number and halve each part.

Example:	$76 \div 2$	Think of 76 as 70 + 6

$$\frac{1}{2} \text{ of } 70 = 35$$

$$\frac{1}{2} \text{ of } 6 = 3$$

$$\text{So } 76 \div 2 = (35 + 3) = 38$$

$4 = 2 \times 2$ and $\frac{1}{4} = \frac{1}{2}$ of a $\frac{1}{2}$

To **divide by 4**, **divide by 2** and **divide by 2 again**.

Example:	$68 \div 4$

$$68 \div 2 = 34 \text{ and } 34 \div 2 = 17$$

$$\text{So } 68 \div 4 = 17$$

$8 = 2 \times 2 \times 2$ and $\frac{1}{8} = \frac{1}{2}$ of a $\frac{1}{4}$ or $\frac{1}{2}$ of a $\frac{1}{2}$ of a $\frac{1}{2}$

To **divide by 8**, **divide by 2**, **divide by 2** and **divide by 2 again!**

Example:	$96 \div 8$

$$96 \div 2 = 48 \text{ and } 48 \div 2 = 24 \text{ and } 24 \div 2 = 12$$

$$\text{So } 96 \div 8 = 12$$

Division using multiples of 10

You can think of division as repeated subtraction. Start by subtracting multiples of 10

Example:	$84 \div 3$	
	84	
	$- \quad 30$	(10 lots of 3)
	54	
	$- \quad 30$	(10 lots of 3)
	24	
	$- \quad 24$	(8 lots of 3)
	00	
	So $84 \div 3 = 28$ (10 + 10 + 8)	

Exercise 26.11 : Division

Now that you have come to the end of the book you should have a very good feel for the way numbers behave and know how exciting it can be when you discover yet another way of playing around with them.

I look forward to meeting you again in *Junior Maths Book 3*!

Index

   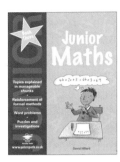

Galore Park

So you _really_ want to learn

GALORE PARK

    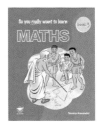

  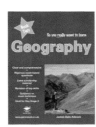  

- Many titles endorsed by the Independent Schools Examination Board

- Perfect for 11+, 13+ and scholarship entrance exam preparation

- Contains explanations and exercises for a complete learning and revision resource

- Developed specifically for those in independent education

- Questions styled for Common Entrance exam preparation

- Suitable for the specialist or non specialist teacher or parent

Independent Schools Examinations Board

For more information please visit our website:
www.galorepark.co.uk

   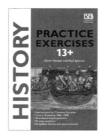 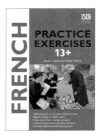
   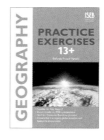 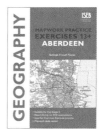

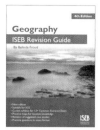